No Country for Engineers

H.G. Evans is a retired, chartered engineer who was employed by various British and American companies in a variety of roles concerned with production, product development, project and factory management, factory expansions and factory relocations.

He has worked in the UK, the US, Canada, Germany, Italy, Spain, Poland, and Japan.

H G Evans

No Country for Engineers

Olympia Publishers
London

www.olympiapublishers.com
OLYMPIA PAPERBACK EDITION

A CIP catalogue record for this title is
available from the British Library.

ISBN: 978-1-84897-409-8

(Olympia Publishers is part of Ashwell Publishing Ltd)

First Published in 2014

Olympia Publishers
60 Cannon Street
London
EC4N 6NP

Printed in Great Britain

This book is dedicated to my family; those deceased, those alive, and those yet unborn.

It is also dedicated to you the reader for your curiosity in picking up this book.

CONTENTS

PREFACE

Just before Christmas 2009 there was an article in the *Daily Telegraph* concerning the UK automotive industry. The article included a comment made by the then BMW chief executive Bernd Pischetsrieder ten years earlier in 1999:

'You British are involved in an interesting experiment of basing your economy on cutting each other's hair, you will excuse us if we in Germany keep our manufacturing jobs.'

The article caused me to reflect upon another seemingly trivial event that occurred 50 years earlier in 1959.

In 1959 I was a student apprentice on a five-year sandwich course. One day in the college library, I was attempting to understand the thermodynamics and forces associated with steam and gas turbines, when, for a moment of light relief I picked up a copy of a small book titled, *Parkinson's Law or the Pursuit of Progress*. The author was C Northcote Parkinson. I did not put the book down until I had read it. The book was basically about bureaucracy in the business world, and started with the sentence, 'Work expands so as to fill the time available for its completion'. The second chapter of the book, titled The Short List or Principles of Selection, contrasted the various methods used for selecting suitable personnel. The overriding assumption of the British method was that a classical education, Oxford especially, would fit any candidate for any administrative post, whereas a scientific education would fit a candidate for nothing, except possibly science. In spite of this apt revelation, which made me wonder whether or not I had made a wise career choice,

I persisted with my engineering studies, which ultimately led to me earning a living in variety of roles within various manufacturing companies, working in various countries that included the UK, Italy, Germany and France. Other countries visited in the course of my career included Canada, USA, Japan, Spain and Poland.

This book attempts to explain the economic position that the UK finds itself in the world today by means of a series of anecdotes concerning the work experiences of myself, a retired UK Chartered Engineer, combined with historical events and decisions that were unique to the UK.

The book consists of a series of self-contained chapters, the titles of which are self-explanatory, and should be of interest to anyone contemplating or participating in a working environment, particularly in manufacturing, and even more particularly as an engineer in the UK.

H G Evans
December 2012

Section A

PREPARATION FOR WORK

'The schools of the country are its future in miniature'
Chinese Proverb

THE LOCAL CHIP SHOP
(An academy for life?)

In the late 1940s following the war, food rationing in the UK was a fact of life. My parents ran an off-licence situated at the end of a block of terraced houses. Our family lived on the premises. Directly opposite where we lived, across the main road, also at the end of a block of terraced houses, was a chip shop. The chip shop was a focal point and was always busy. It was the one place one could purchase a hot meal or snack without the need for food coupons. Chips, (nowadays called French fries), were in fact the staple food of many families.

The chip shop was overlooked from the bedroom that I shared with my brother, and we would often observe the activities on the chip shop premises. Seen from my eyes, a primary school boy at the time, the person I most recall was a large jovial fat man who rarely bought chips but who was always the centre of attention. The man always wore an oversize jacket, with oversize pockets that were always bulging with money in the form of loose change. When I asked my mother who the man was, and why did he always seem to have so much money, she told me that he collected money from people who bet on horse races, and that he worked for someone whose activities were somewhat dubious and illegal. My mother also told me that I would never have any money if I indulged in such activities when I grew up.

One day whilst I was in the chip shop, a customer mentioned to the proprietor that he was feeling ill and asked for advice. Following some banter, the proprietor suggested that he ask the large fat man who was hanging around in the background. The fat man upon being asked, by the customer, replied with the question, "What was it that made you ill?" The proprietor then grinned and said to his customer: "There you are. I told you, whatever made you ill will make you better." I recall thinking at the time that this advice, if enacted, could not possibly work as I visualised that someone suffering from a dose of arsenic could not expect to get better by consuming even more arsenic.

Many years later, the young impressionable boy that I was, has grown into a man close to old age. I often wonder at what stage I will revert into my second childhood, and more to the point will I recognize the fact when, and if I do.

The off-licence that I grew up in as a child and the chip shop that I knew have long since disappeared. They have been replaced with a plethora of alternatives that perform the same functions but on a much larger scale. The same applies to that fat man. He has also been replaced on an even larger scale with a plethora of alternatives, except that his formerly dubious associated activities have been legalised, and it is now regarded as normal to participate in them.

Today, the UK and most of the western world is heavily in debt and in the throes of a major financial crisis. At a national level it is proposed that the solution of our debt crisis is to borrow money, and, in the event that this does not work, to borrow even more money. At a personal level I am encouraged in a variety of ways to gamble with the money that I currently possess. The proposed solutions bring to mind the advice of my mother regarding my observations of the fat man in the chip shop, and the day in the chip shop when I heard: "Whatever made you ill will make you better."

It would appear that I have reverted to my second childhood, and more to the point seem to be fully aware of it. I also suspect that the local chip shop, without knowing it, was in effect an academy, an academy for life.

COPYING, JAPAN, WOODWORK AND PHYSICS
(Re-engineering?)

At the end of WWII the Allies confiscated German patents and made them available to the general public. As a result of experiencing a shortage of quality cameras during the war, the UK military decided that they needed a camera comparable to the Leica and took the design drawings from the Leitz factory in Wetzlar. The company who produced the resultant copy was Reid & Sigrist Ltd, a manufacturer of aircraft parts and precision instruments based in Leicester. The resultant Reid camera was announced in May 1947 but was not available until 1951. Production lasted until 1964 when Reid & Sigrist ceased camera production and sold remaining parts to A W Young Ltd of London. Two variants were produced, the Reid III, which was a copy of the Leica III series and the Reid I which was a copy of the Leica E. Both copies had deficiencies compared with the original Leica models.

In the early 1950s woodwork was one of the subjects taught at the grammar school I attended. The woodwork class was situated in the basement of the school and was well equipped with a lathe, benches and carpentry tools, as one would expect for such a practical subject. The pleasant smell of wood-glue and wood shavings was always present in the classroom. The woodwork teacher was both practical and straightforward in dealing with his pupils. I recall one day the subject of Japan arose and in particular his comment at the time, which went something along the lines of: "Japan is a nation of copiers, they are not original and creative thinkers, unlike us British, and consequently will never be a real industrial power." It was a commonly held view in the UK at the time.

The two physics laboratories were also situated in the school basement and they too were well equipped to enable pupils to confirm in practical ways the various mathematical theories within their subject matter. The physics teacher was also practical and straightforward in his dealings with pupils. The physics teacher was a very keen photographer. One day when the subject of optics and optical systems were being studied, the topic of Japanese cameras arose and the physics teacher said something along the lines of: "Some of you may think that the Japanese copy everything, but you may be surprised to know that the Leica camera currently use Japanese lenses, and will continue to do so until their own lenses are as good." I recall thinking that the woodwork teacher may have underestimated the Japanese in that they may have started off by copying but they had ended up producing something superior to the original.

In the 1960s the proceedings of The Institution of Mechanical Engineers were readily available for student, graduate and members for little or no cost. I recall reading from one such article about the inability of UK Engineering manufacturers to produce cost effective precision components, quoting the Leica camera copy as an example. The implications were that UK manufacturing capability was inadequate to cope with the modern era. If the UK was incapable of copying effectively, it could hardly be expected to improve a copied product, an issue that the Japanese clearly didn't suffer from.

Many years later in the early 1990s, I was driving down the A1 motorway after having visited a Japanese car plant in the North East of England. I had a Japanese passenger alongside me. The reason that my passenger was Japanese was that his company was our equivalent in Japan. We both supplied the same car manufacturer who had car plants in both Japan and the UK. To supply a Japanese car manufacturer a UK supplier had to form an agreement with their equivalent supplier in Japan. The Japanese supplier was then used to help ensure that the manufacturing standards of the UK supplier matched those in Japan. In essence the UK supplier copied the practices of the Japanese supplier. As we were continuing our journey, we passed Teesside and my passenger noticed the huge petrochemical complex on our left hand side in the distance, and asked me what it was. I answered, and expanded a little on the industrial historical background of the area in general. My Japanese companion then said something along the lines of:

"*You* were once on top in such things, but that was then. *We* are the masters now."

It made me recall the comments of my past woodwork teacher and wondering whether he would have believed it possible that Japan would be in such a position compared to the UK. He was certainly wrong with respect to Japan but it could be argued that he was correct in his belief that it mattered for a country to have an effective and strong industrial presence.

Re-engineering is not copying. It could also be argued that the Japanese concept 'kaizen', or continuous improvement, was never truly understood nor practised in UK Industry. Resting on one's laurels, on the other hand, certainly was.

CLEARING THE AIR
(Is seeing believing?)

During my childhood the basic fuel for heating houses was coal. Coal was transported from coal pits via rail to railway sidings, which were situated at numerous locations on the substantial rail network that existed after World War II.

Coal merchants used lorries or horses and carts to transport coal from the sidings to individual houses. Coal was also used in the production of coal gas, the residue of which was coke. Coke was also used as a fuel and could be obtained directly from the local gas works. Coal was also the main fuel used to power the steam driven generators that provided electricity and the fuel that powered the steam engines used on the railways. Coal and its by-products were also the basis of the dye and chemical industries. In short coal, the mainstay of the Industrial Revolution, provided gas, electricity, coke and a myriad of other products in addition to being a fuel in its own right.

Smoke from coal fires was a feature of everyday life and many people living in towns and cities suffered respiratory problems, particularly in winter. In 1952 the public outcry following the Great Smog of London resulted in the Clean Air Act 1956. The Act introduced measures that aimed to reduce the amount of smoke pollution from household fires, the location of power stations away from cities, increased chimney heights, and moves to cleaner solid fuels, electricity and gas.

At the grammar school I attended, part of the education in the science sixth form was a period devoted to 'Liberal Studies', the aim of which was to help us appreciate the finer things in life that the narrow topics of mathematics, physics and chemistry were considered to deny us. Our liberal studies teacher was Miss Southern who was well-spoken, well-mannered and well-educated, in the classical sense. I believe Miss Southern regarded us as rough diamonds at best.

The above events, one may have thought, would have meant little to myself, a student in the science sixth form, however, one day Miss Southern tasked the class to write an essay on the Clean Air Act 1956. The Town Council were to give prizes for the best essays and the competition was open to all schools in the town. I recall being rather pleased with my essay as I gave it to Miss Southern and thought no more about it.

Some weeks later I was informed that I was one of the winners and that I had to go to the Town Hall to receive a prize. The Town Hall situated in the town centre was within ten minutes walking distance from the school. The competition winners were ushered into a room where we came face to face with the appropriate council committee consisting of councillors and Town Hall staff. I recognised Dr Monks, my local doctor and future mayor. There were 18 winners ranging in ages 12 to 18 years. Seventeen of the 18 winners were from the grammar school of which I was a pupil. The exception was a bespectacled 13-year-old boy from a secondary modern school situated near to where I lived. First, second and third prizes were awarded to each age group. The secondary modern schoolboy won second prize in his age group. I was pleased to receive first prize in my age group especially as the second and third prizes went to my peers from the arts sixth form. Following the simple presentation, one of the councillors left his seat, ran across the floor, profusely shook the hand of the secondary modern school boy, congratulated him, and said:

"I've always said that the secondary modern schools are as good as the grammar schools, this just proves it."

I don't remember what the prize was, but I certainly remembered the actions and words of that councillor. The councillor could have said: 'You my young lad should be at the grammar school'. He didn't, his actions on the other hand clearly said: 'you and I didn't go to a grammar school. We are both as good as anyone, and I will not let what I see in front of me dissuade me from my lifelong belief that grammar schools should be abolished.'

Like-minded politicians of that councillor were subsequently instrumental in abolishing grammar schools along with their associated selection process. The state grammar schools were replaced with mixed ability state comprehensive secondary schools, as were the state secondary modern schools.

A few years later the pupils and staff of the grammar school that I attended were relocated to a new building on the outskirts of the town and, shortly afterwards, the school was renamed as a comprehensive school. The original grammar school, an imposing Victorian building, built to educate the 'brighter' working classes, now consists of living apartments.

DON'T BELIEVE EVERYTHING
IN THE NEWSPAPERS
(Not even in the business section?)

In my early teens I became interested in cycle road racing and tried to keep abreast of continental cycle events such as the Giro d'Italia and the Tour de France. At the time, road race cycling in the UK was organised by two bitter contrasting factions. One faction consisted of the established National Cyclists Union (NCU), formed in 1893, and the Road Time Trials Council (RTTC), formed in 1937. Members of this faction specialised in track racing and individual time trials. The second faction was the upstart British League of Racing Cyclists (BLRC), formed in 1942 whose members specialised in continental style massed start road races.

In 1952 the BLRC sent a road racing team to participate behind the Iron Curtain in the Warsaw-Berlin-Prague Road Race (Subsequently called the Peace Race). A Scot, Ian Steel, won the 1952 Race, and the British team won the team event. The victory was spoiled somewhat as Ian Steel was not allowed to perform a lap of honour.

The following year I was impatient to see how the British team were performing, and as the family newspaper did not feature cycle racing in the sports section, I decided to cycle to the town library to read the *Daily Worker*, a communist party paper, whose contents I was sure would give me the results of the previous day's stage race. The town library had every newspaper published, and I settled down to read the *Daily Worker*, (subsequently renamed the *Morning Star*). The pages describing the event included numerous photos of the East European riders who were lauded for their exploits of the day. There were no photos or mention of the British riders, which rather surprised me. (With hindsight I should have realised that there was a Cold War on, and the British riders were possibly perceived as capitalist toadies masquerading as cyclists.) Disappointed, I decided to look at all the other papers in the library and went through every newspaper that was published that day. The information I required was found in the sports section of the *Daily Telegraph*. I cycled home pondering how a simple cycle race could be portrayed in such different ways depending on which newspaper you happened to read.

On Monday, November 23, 1998, I was reading the *Daily Telegraph* when I recognised a photo of Mr E B Stephens, the retired Chairman and Chief Executive of the Engineering Conglomerate Siebe PLC. The photo was in the 'This Week' column of the business news. The column had two photos. The first photo was that of Mr Stephens, underneath of which was the caption, 'Pylon pressure: National Grid set for profits fall.' The second photo showed three electricity pylons, and had the caption, 'Looking stronger: Allen Yurko, Chief of Siebe.' It would have been obvious to the readers that the captions under each photograph were the wrong way round. However, how many of the readers would have recognised that the photograph pertaining to be Allen Yurko was in fact Mr E Barry Stephens?

Don't believe everything you read or even see in the newspapers, not even in the business section.

Section B

WORK EXPERIENCE

'Work spares us from three great evils: boredom, vice and need.'
Francois Marie Arouet de Voltaire
1694-1778

B1

INTERNAL COMMUNICATION
(Do you know what is going on?)

In the early 1960s I spent three months at Berkeley Nuclear Power Station as part of my industrial training programme. Berkeley was one of seven sites constituting Britain's nuclear power programme that used the magnox fuel element, a rod of uranium metal canned in a magnesium alloy. At the time the British nuclear power programme was the largest in the world and planned for an electrical capacity of 5,000 MW by 1968, and a further 5,000 MW by 1975[1]. (Equivalent to 3,400 fully operating wind turbines today.) The principle of generating electricity was relatively simple. Heat generated by nuclear reaction was transferred to carbon dioxide that passed through the reactor via graphite blocks that contained the magnox fuel elements. The heated carbon dioxide was then passed through water via heat exchangers creating steam, which in turn then passed through turbines attached to alternators, which generated electricity.

Berkeley Nuclear Power Station comprised two reactors, and during my time there, was being prepared to go active and become the first nuclear power station in the UK to generate electricity solely for the National Grid.

Carbon dioxide entered the base of each reactor via four large diameter ducts and passed though channels in carbon graphite blocks stacked inside the reactor. Each channel contained aluminium cylinders containing uranium fuel pellets. The carbon dioxide left the reactor in one of four, large diameter ducts, situated in the roof of the reactor. Access to the reactor was attained by entering one of the outlet ducts, crawling along the duct until you reached the inlet, at which point you could drop down on to the reactor floor.

I expressed a wish to go inside a reactor and shortly afterwards I, along with others, were taken into a preparation room where we were told to strip naked and asked to remove any potentially loose objects such as false teeth. We were then issued with white one-piece suits. The precautions taken were to ensure that no loose or foreign bodies would be left inside the reactor, as they would potentially contaminate sensor readings, strategically situated within the reactor itself. To enable us to see, we were each given what could best be described as an electric miners lamp, wrapped in tape to ensure that any loose fittings on the lamp were secure. Upon reaching the reactor face one saw what appeared to be a circular kitchen floor with square graphite tiles, from which protruded at regular intervals what appeared to be lamp posts connecting the floor to the concave shaped reactor roof. These posts were in fact solid steel control rods, each of which could be raised and lowered independently from the charge face through the reactor roof and into the body of the reactor. The purpose of the control rods was to control the speed of neutrons produced by nuclear fission. The holes or channels containing the 'magnox' fuel containers were clearly visible. After spending a little time observing activities I left the reactor face, happy in the knowledge that I could boast to my future unborn children that their dad had stood on the reactor face of the first atomic power station in the UK.

A few weeks after my little adventure there were noticeable signs of unusual activity in the reactor building. Upon listening to the gossip in the site canteen it appeared that a wing nut from one of the 'miners lamps' had fallen off and disappeared down one of the graphite block holes ending up on the reactor base.

Upon searching for the wing nut using state of the art viewfinders, the observers, to their horror, noticed a considerable quantity of discarded welding rod tips and cigarette ends, along with the odd spanner, although I hasten to add that the latter could have been an exaggeration.

When I left the site, one lesson that this episode had brought home to me was the realisation of the massive gap between those at the top issuing orders and procedures, and those at the front face supposedly carrying them out.

References:

[1]*Kempe's Engineers Year Book 1969*. Vol.2 Nuclear Energy. Page 419.

B2

INCENTIVES
(Output will increase, won't it?)

As part of my industrial training in 1960, I worked in a foundry in the Midlands for three months. A portion of the work experience consisted of labouring for a Moulder who was paid for the number of castings that he produced. The Moulder was paid a price for each moulding made under a system of payment known as piecework. The price was fixed by a Rate-fixer in agreement with the Moulder. For any new casting the negotiation on the foundry floor could take considerable time before an agreement was reached, as the price agreed would be fixed for future production of that particular casting.

On one particular day a new casting had to be made. I stood by and watched as the discussion between the Rate-fixer and the Moulder ensued before the price was agreed. The time taken to reach agreement was approximately half an hour during which time the Rate-fixer became noticeably agitated. When the Rate-fixer had left I naïvely asked the Moulder how he would make up the lost time. He grinned, and proceeded to make the number of castings that he considered necessary to give him his optimum payment for the day. I was astounded when he informed me an hour before the end of his shift that we were finished for the day. I pointed out to him that he could make more castings and earn more money, to which he replied that he had no intention of earning money to pay the taxman. He had earned enough for the day. The Rate-fixer came back later to see what had been produced and was not pleased to see the result. He considered that he had been outsmarted.

On the shop floor, piecework was always contentious wherever I saw it in use as a payment system. Management invariably thought differently, as they considered it obvious that it would encourage greater output.

During the 1980s I was employed as the Manufacturing Manager of a rubber company that made a multitude of rubber moulded and extruded products. When I joined the company the payment of the workers was highly biased to a piecework system where the greater part of the take home pay was earned by piecework. I noticed that some of the more productive workers would finish early and go to the canteen before clocking out. Recalling my experience in the foundry, I thought that I would improve productivity by increasing exponentially the piece rate for parts made after a certain quantity had been produced. I reasoned that this would ensure that the operators would work to the end of their shift and the company would have an increase in production. To my surprise I noticed this did not make the slightest difference. When I discussed this with the operators pointing out what they were missing, they told me that they would be working for the taxman and preferred to rest before going home. The operators decided themselves what they considered was their optimum take-home pay. Those operators who were not as adept in their techniques as their more productive peers invariably tried to cheat the system one way or another. Examples would be claiming to have produced more than they had, or changing machine set parameters.

Nowadays the UK is awash with different forms of incentives all of which are intended to produce better performances from those participating in them, than would otherwise be the case. Bankers have their bonus schemes, as do chief executives, managers and soccer players to name but a few; even those out of work are considered to require incentives to get them back to work.

When I reached the stage of being in a position to benefit from an incentive scheme, how did I react myself? I exploited the rules. I have no doubt that is what everybody would do in a similar situation.

Currently, incentives appear to be out of control, they are based on the belief that people are basically lazy whose goals run counter to the organisation in which they work. To use the parlance of the behavioural sociologist Douglas Macgregor, such organisations believe people conform to *Theory X*[1].

In the first year of my sandwich course industrial training I first became aware of Elton Mayo and the Hawthorne Studies[1], which made me conclude that you can get away with almost anything with your workforce, provided that you show an interest in them.

It could be argued that incentives are a smokescreen and are irrelevant to the wellbeing of any organisation. To express this in another way, I believe that I too could have ruined any one of the many companies that now litter UK industrial graveyards. I would have been satisfied with half the salary and without any knighthoods being bestowed upon me, as was often the case with many of the Chief Executive Officers of those now defunct UK companies.

The reader has only my word for this as I was never in a position to ruin whole companies for my own personal benefit.

References:

[1] *Organizational Psychology*. Edgar H Schein. Prentice-Hall Inc.

SUGGESTION BOXES
(Japan OK. UK?)

As a generalisation it is widely acknowledged that in Japan, employee involvement via the use of suggestion boxes is widely used and very effective.

In the UK, other than in Japanese plants, suggestion boxes are a rarity.

During the early days of my career I participated in introducing and trying to implement the use of suggestion boxes. In the second job of my career, in the 1960s I was a Process Development Engineer in the dyestuffs division of a large chemical company where I became a member of a committee set up to vet employee suggestions. The committee consisted of staff from the various company departments, namely, processing, personnel, engineering, work-study, technical and accountancy.

Union shop stewards were also members. There were many unions on the site and there would often be many shop stewards who would expect to be involved. In the event that there were potentially more shop stewards than staff members, additional members of staff would be added so that there was always a majority of management representatives. This action ensured that any decision made during the committee meetings did not contradict management wishes. The meetings invariably produced masses of hot air and resulted in few decisions. After a period of time suggestions invariably dried up and the suggestion boxes became disused, save for the odd unsigned suggestion that if certain management members were fired or even whole departments closed down, the company would save a fortune. Such suggestions were of course ignored, and the boxes were eventually removed. With hindsight, some of those unsigned suggestions would have saved a small fortune. Many similar companies ultimately employed management consultants at great expense, with the result that even more drastic measures were suggested and implemented.

Many years later in the 1990s, I visited a relatively new Japanese car plant in the UK. I noticed several suggestion boxes around the premises, and, with the above in mind, casually asked how they managed to run what was clearly a successful suggestion scheme. It was explained to me that every new employee completed a structured training programme that involved the replication of car track situations. During training, the trainee would be told of the importance of shop floor suggestions and that they would be encouraged to participate in them. On the completion of their training the first job on the track would be a relatively simple task. An example would be the fitting of two wheels on one side of a car as it passed by the appropriate workstation on the car assembly track. The actions required to do this task are similar to what you, the reader, would do in replacing a punctured tyre, except that instead of using a hand held socket spanner, the operator was provided with a pneumatic socket spanner connected to an overhead air line via an air hose. The length of air hose, fitted with quick release connections at either end, would be supplied deliberately short, such that the operator would not be able to take full advantage of the length of time available to him or her as the car passed their workstation. At the end of the shift, the operator would be asked how things had gone on during their first day, and asked if there was anything that they could think of that might make their task easier. The response would invariably be along the lines of, "You could give me a longer hose."

The operator would be congratulated on coming up with their first suggestion and would be given a nominal cash award, and told that more suggestions would be expected in future. In the unlikely event that the operator did not come up with the anticipated reply the operator would be left to continue with the short hose and the whole cycle of events would be repeated.

All suggestions received an award.

DRINK
(Can drink at work serve a purpose?)

The sight of drunks in British cities, towns and villages is a common occurrence and results in an increased attendance at weekends in the A&E departments at our hospitals. There is much hand wringing and hot air expended on what we regard as an Anglo-Saxon phenomena and our inability to do anything about it. Drink is often used as a means of relaxation on social occasions. When taken in excess people lose their inhibitions.

In the late 1960s, as the Mechanical Engineer of a petroleum-chemical plant in Scotland, I was invited along with other members of staff, to the company Christmas party. The invitation was for staff only. Drink we were told would be unlimited. One would have thought that alarm bells should have rung inside the heads of anyone invited.

At the function it was noticeable for anyone who cared to observe, that two people were not drinking. The two people were the Plant Manager and a Director from Head Office. Church bells should have rung inside everybody's heads, but no, most kept on drinking, and, as time progressed, became more boisterous. More than one staff member told the Plant Manager what they thought of him in terms that would normally be considered inadvisable. Previously discrete affairs between certain staff members became noticeably indiscrete and boorish drunken behaviour became the norm for others.

The following week wholesale changes were made in the company, all of which could be related to the behaviour of those participating in the party. The company had achieved this reorganisation without having to spend one penny on Management Consultants.

In the 1970s, when in Italy, the General Manager (GM) to whom I reported was an Irish-American. I was aware that he probably was a Republican because he sometimes had an elephant brooch in his coat lapel. His daughter, a Democrat supporter, mentioned to me that he wanted to vote for J F Kennedy in the USA presidential elections, but did not do so because the President of the parent American Company was a staunch Republican.

One evening, I was with the GM in a hotel in Milan when our conversation veered towards politics. Aware of the above, I mentioned the War, Churchill, and the co-operation between the USA and the UK. The GM then reminisced about his war years telling me he recalled dancing with a beautiful woman who complimented him by saying, "You dance beautifully, just like an English gentleman." He then continued to tell me, "I'd never been so insulted in my life." My immediate thoughts went along the lines of, 'Good grief, my career is dependant on this fellow,' but I recall saying something along the lines of, "Hmmm, my mother is Irish," and steered the conversation quickly on to another topic.

A few weeks later we were in Milan where we had gone to pick up the GM's wife and where, at the same hotel, the subject turned to the religious situation in Northern Ireland. I, being aware of where his sympathies were likely to be, suggested that Eire, unlike Northern Ireland did not have a problem because the religious minority were small and were perceived to pose no threat. His wife then said, "He might have a point there," whereupon the GM immediately turned on his wife and snarled, " Don't you dare take anyone else's side whilst I'm in discussion."

Drink can serve a purpose when taken in moderation and also when taken in excess. Drink can clearly be used as an aid in determining what people really think in terms they would not normally disclose.

The main lesson learned from the above, is the importance of getting on the same wavelength of anybody you wish to influence. This is one of the reasons why those at the top appear to be surrounded by sycophants, and also why Management Consultants are so successful.

OUT OF SIGHT OUT OF MIND
(Think before you leap?)

In the late 1960s I was working for an American company as a Production Development Engineer. It was during this time that I had my first visit to Canada and the USA. The objective of the visit was for me to observe production methods, processes and equipment that could be implemented in the UK, in order to improve productivity.

At that time, travelling to North America was almost an adventure, the amount of money taken out of the country had to be declared using a form PP/32 titled, 'Foreign Exchange Facilities Business, Professional, Official and Forces Travel Exchange Control Act 1947.' A non-immigrant visa was also required. The amount of money I took was £135.

At one of the Canadian plants that I visited it was very noticeable that most of the top and middle management had German names. The town in which the plant was situated had, during the First World War, changed its name from that of a German city to that of a famous British General. During the many topics that were discussed over dinner, the subject of the apparent imbalance of the management was touched upon. It became clear that those who had volunteered for service in the Second World War, on their return, found that they had missed possible promotion to those who had not volunteered.

Variations of this observation were noticeable at all levels in the many organisations that I subsequently worked for throughout my career.

Out of sight out of mind. Think before you leap.

B6

BRITISH STANDARDS
(What does the colour blue represent?)

In the mid 1960s I started employment in a continuous process plant as the Plant Mechanical Engineer, the same day as did as the Plant Services Engineer.

The plant was situated in Scotland. The Head Office was situated in a similar larger plant in the south of England.

All personnel on the site had to wear white safety helmets. The helmets that my colleague and I were issued with had a blue band around the helmet perimeter to denote that we were from the Engineering Department. The helmets also had a blue band that ran from back to front that signified that we were members of staff. The colours for the Production and Technical personnel were green and yellow respectively. In short, you could walk through the site and know the job function and status of anyone you met.

All the pipe work on the site was painted silver-grey. My colleague, the plant services engineer, decided that in the main services area he would have the pipes identified by being painted with the appropriate British Standard marking. This action would enable him, and others, to identify the many liquids and gases that the pipes contained. These included, compressed air, hexane, water, cooling water, steam, liquid carbon dioxide, town gas and various refrigerants. He also arranged for an office to be built in the main services area.

Some of the gases and liquids involved in the process were highly flammable and fires were a frequent occurrence. This feature had not gone unnoticed elsewhere. We learned from one supplier, for example, who, having asked directions to the plant, had been told to wait a couple of minutes and follow the fire engine that was certain to pass by.

During the stoppages that occurred, plant modifications, maintenance and other work would be carried out at short notice.

As one can imagine the unscheduled downtimes were such that the plant had difficulty in meeting customer delivery promises. During one such unscheduled shutdown, the exasperated Chief Executive informed the Plant Manager that he would fly up from Head Office in order to find out for himself what was going on.

The news of his impending visit created panic, not only because the gentleman concerned was known for his short temper and did not suffer fools gladly, (that meant anybody but himself), but because the plant would not be operational as a result of which someone would be held responsible and fired.

The Chief Executive arrived and was taken on a conducted tour where everything appeared to be in order. This was achieved by a complex signalling system whereby each separate section of the process was arranged to work whilst he passed through it, thereby ceasing immediately afterwards.

On arriving at the Engineering Services area the Chief Executive looked at the almost completed office, and enquired, "To whom does that office belong?" On being told it was the Services Engineer, he bellowed, "Pull it down. An engineer's place is on the plant not in the office." He then looked at the pipes that were painted and marked to British Standard specification colours and bellowed, "What's that?" and upon being told, continued with his rant, "Engineering is blue, paint those pipes blue." My colleague, the Plant Services Engineer certainly felt blue in addition to being nonplussed.

A few years later, sometime after I had left that company, I read in a technical journal that the aforementioned Chief Executive had retired after having received a prestigious award for his services to the industry.

WHEN IN ROME DO AS THE ROMANS DO
(Stale bread in Italy?)

In the early 1970s, I became a Project Manager, responsible for the transfer and setting up of the production facilities of a factory from Scotland to Italy. The transfer was part of an agreement between the American company for whom I worked, and an Italian company. The American company had sold their premises situated near the centre of Edinburgh and were looking for new premises for what was a profitable product in a growing market. The Italian company had moved part of their manufacturing facilities from a landlocked site, situated on the outskirts of Milan, to a new plant in the south of Italy. The Italian company wished for a partnership at the new plant. As part of the agreement it had been decided to have an American as the first General Manager of the completed factory. The initial choice of the American company for the post was an Italian-American. Unfortunately their first choice could not persuade his wife to move to Italy. The result was that the first General Manager of the joint venture was an Irish-American.

My Italian counterpart was fluent in German and French, but spoke no English. My means of communicating with him was in French. The top Italian who was the Plant Director spoke fluent English, French & German, in addition to his mother tongue. He was also a fully qualified Engineer (Dott.Ing). None of the small British group, other than myself, could speak any language other than their own, and the same applied to the Americans, in particular, the new General Manager.

At the first get to know everybody dinner, involving the Americans, Italians and the British, an appropriate restaurant worthy of the occasion was chosen. As one can imagine, special care was taken over the seating arrangements. As I sat down, my Italian counterpart said to me (in French), "Do what I do."

The Italians were both flamboyant and courteous in managing their guests, to the extent that the Italian plant production manager took the tray of bread from the head waiter when it appeared, and proceeded with great gusto and flourish to present the bread to the Americans, accompanied by thunderous applause from the Italians. When the bread tray arrived to me I was on the point of picking up a piece of bread when I received a kick from underneath the table from my 'Italian colleague', who said when I looked at him, "The bread, I told you, do as I do." I chose the bread type he had, and after the bread tray passed on, said to him, "What was all that about?" He then told me that some of the bread was three days old. As I looked around the table it dawned on me that the Italians were eating fresh bread, whilst the non-Italians were eating stale bread, apart from one, who was suffering from a sore shin.

When in Rome do as the Romans do.

LANGUAGES
(Everyone speaks English, don't they?)

The majority of native-born students that leave the UK state educational system are not multilingual. It could even be argued that a significant minority cannot even speak English properly. In my working experience whenever I heard grammatically correct English spoken it would often be someone emanating from the Dutch or Scandinavian state educational system.

In the early 1970s I became Project Manager responsible for the transfer of the manufacturing facilities of a factory in Scotland to a new factory site in Italy. On the Italian site there were many contractors occupied with building extensions, engineering services, and the installation of machinery. The contractors were controlled by my Italian equivalent with whom I communicated in French. On site I soon became a familiar face on nodding terms with the Italian workforce.

One day I was approached by one of the contractor's workmen, who, to my surprise, spoke very good English, and thereafter I spoke to him whenever I saw him on site.

One day whilst in the office at my desk, sitting opposite my Italian colleague, the Irish-American General Manager (GM) approached me, stopped, and asked me to ask my Italian colleague why he had allowed the contractors to have "done such and such", referring to some minor technical matter. My Italian colleague in reply, told me to tell the GM that he would see to the matter concerned immediately. When the GM left us, my Italian colleague said to me, "That will be that English speaking Italian workman."

Shortly afterwards the 'Italian contractor workman' approached me at my desk clearly upset. He had just been fired by his employer and asked me to try and persuade my Italian colleague, sat opposite me, to change his mind, as he believed that my colleague was responsible. My efforts on his behalf were met by an indifferent shrug of the shoulders. When the workman, almost in tears, left the two of us, I continued the dialogue with my Italian colleague by suggesting how unjust his actions had been. My Italian colleague eventually looked at me and said, "You will be interested to know that I will fire every English speaking contractor on site, and, if *you* cause me any trouble I will fire the French speaking ones too."

I often ruminated over this event. The Italian workman had lost his job by thinking he was furthering his prospects by his command of English. The GM lost useful contacts on the shop floor without realising it. My Italian colleague had shown his power and influence over me, whilst at the same time deliberately weakening the General Manager's influence over himself.

The overriding lesson I learned was the importance of being able to understand the language of the inhabitants of the country you are working in.

Everyone does not speak English.

THE POLITICAL COMMISSAR
(Do you wish to pay for the wine?)

During the early 1970s when in Italy, the joint company for whom I was working, became aware of an interesting innovation concerning our product that had been developed in an East European country. The country concerned at the time was behind the Iron Curtain. The Italian Plant Director and the British Product Technician were sent to investigate. They returned two days later.

A return visit had been arranged and I informed my Italian counterpart, who was considerably older than me, saying something along the lines, "We are going to get a return visit by a couple of their people." My Italian colleague replied saying, "A couple? You are joking, there will be at least six," and proceeded to tell me that there would be the Technician concerned, the Technician's immediate boss, the Plant Manager, the Sales Manager, the Accounts Manager and the Political Commissar. I recall bursting out laughing saying, "The Political Commissar, *you* must be joking."

He then said, "You clearly don't understand the system, there will be a Political Commissar and what is more it will be a woman." At this stage I said he was being ridiculous and we ended with a lively discussion resulting in a wager, whereby the loser would present the winner with a bottle of wine at dinner. (We all lived at the time in a state run hotel.)

We were waiting for dinner when our visitors came down the stairs. We both watched as they came into the dining room one after the other. There were six of them, five of whom were men. I thought that the odds were still in my favour and watched intently as introductions were made. We sat down for dinner. At dinner all the questions we asked were answered, after a nod of approval had been given from the Political Commissar. The Political Commissar was the woman.

I had lost the wager, but it caused me to reflect on the meaning of political interference.

LOOK ON THE BRIGHT SIDE OF LIFE
(Can things get worse?)

In the mid 1970s in a new job, I had spent the morning looking around the large manufacturing premises of the parent company, which, without wishing to mince words, was a Dickensian Victorian slum. Lunchtime arrived, and, as the Human Resources department had not decided which of the five canteens I was entitled to eat in, I decided to have lunch at the local pub, which was called 'The Lancashire Fusiliers'.

Having purchased a sandwich and a tonic water, (not wishing to have beer on my breath), I sat down and contemplated my situation. I had changed my job basically for the status of having a company car. I had sold a lovely house in Scotland and had moved my wife and two young children to a flat in Blackpool, because, in the intervening period, I had failed to find somewhere suitable to live. As I was beginning to feel sorry for myself, for what was apparently a big mistake of my own creation, my gaze left the contents of my glass and I looked around the room. The wallpaper in the room was a dull smoke stained yellow colour upon which was what appeared to be black writing. I got up from my seat and had a closer look. Every wall in the room had names of men of the Lancashire Fusiliers who had died, in their prime, in the First World War.

I recall leaving that public house in a different frame of mind to that when I entered it.

TOILETS
(Are they taken for granted?)

The above topic is not mentioned in any of the many management books that I have read concerning people and organisations. It is a subject that is clearly taken care of by regulations that dictate the minimum facilities required for a given number of employees. What else is there to consider?

I once attended an interview facing two gentlemen. One was from the Production Department the other was from the Engineering Department. During the interview it became apparent that the Production Manager wanted someone who could, or should, have been provided from the Engineering Department, and I asked a question to that effect. The Production Manager noticeably faltered, and the interview continued. At the end of the interview the Engineering Manager invited me to go for a 'break'. I politely refused, passed some pleasantries and left. That weekend at home, whilst reading an extract from the memoirs of Lyndon B Johnson in *The Sunday Times*, my eyes suddenly focussed on a particular sentence in which he was quoted as saying, *"There are two things in life you must remember if you wish to get on."* I cannot recall the first, but I certainly recall the second. *"Never refuse an invitation to the john's."* I recall kicking myself wondering what I had missed as a result of my refusal to go for a 'break'.

In the late 1970s I was the 'Works Manager' of a small factory. Amongst my duties was that of approving minor requisitions. One day, shortly after commencing my job, a requisition appeared in front of me requesting the replacement of a broken toilet seat. I signed it off without a second thought. A week later an identical request appeared. 'This is strange,' I thought, and set off to investigate. The works toilet facilities comprised six cubicles. As the cubicles were vacated, I opened all six doors, and stood back to see if there were any obvious design differences that might explain the phenomena. What was immediately apparent was that there were two types of lavatory, one, clearly of Victorian design, had wooden seats fixed to the pan supplied with water from a cistern near the roof, whereas the more modern design had hinged plastic seats attached to the pan had the cistern integrated with it. It was clear that the problem was not the Victorian design. The problem was with the modern design. Upon further investigation I noticed the inside walls of all the cubicles contained various sketches of dubious artistic merit, in addition to writings most of which were libellous opinions concerning the Managing Director.

As a result of my investigation I concluded, rightly or wrongly, that the breakages were caused by heavy hobnailed boots worn by operators who were sitting on the modern cistern in order that their legs would be unnoticed by any supervisor looking underneath the cubicle walls from one end. This action would enable the operator to read or look at the pictures in *The Sun* newspaper without being disturbed. At the time I recall pondering, 'Do the designers of lavatory systems ever think of such matters?' I also thought the Victorians knew what they were doing.

Today, with Health and Safety regulations in mind, it is clear the Victorian design was defective in the sense that an employee would nowadays probably be awarded damages in the event of suffering an injury whilst attempting to climb up and sit on their type of cistern.

Notwithstanding the general lack of toilet facilities for women, the positioning of shop floor toilet facilities can also be illuminating.

Imagine being an operator on the third floor of a mixing plant with the plant toilets situated on the ground floor 100m away. Imagine the operator suffering from a weak bladder. Imagine too that the components to be mixed consisted of a multitude of absorbent chemicals that were added to the mixer machine. What do you think that operator might do? The result could be the puzzlement of the Quality Assurance Department as they detect intermittent unaccounted increases of uric acid in the mix. Imagine the problem faced by those tasked to find the cause. Think of the suspicions and accusations made against the suppliers, and the dilemma in the event of the suppliers themselves finding the root cause of the problem.

In 1995 my duties included visiting three car assembly plants situated in Germany, Spain and the UK. It was the standard procedure in all three plants to have cars picked at random from the assembly line, taken to a separate building, and inspected for faults. Standard reports concerning the issues found were finalised by the following day, in time for the factory management to discuss the results. The result was that the walls of the room or building set aside for this purpose were covered with charts and photos so that persistent issues could be clearly discerned. The daily meetings usually occurred at midday.

One day at the UK car plant I, along with our German contact and a colleague from one of our plants, were walking from the main building to the Inspection building situated nearby, in order to attend the daily meeting. As we left the main car plant we passed a lean-to building comprising of a roof supported by stanchions, which contained pumps. Not only were the pumps visible but so also was a huge notice, which stated:

'ANYONE FOUND URINATING ON THESE PREMISES WILL BE LIABLE FOR DISCIPLINARY ACTION.'

I stopped, pointed this out to the German and said, "If you want to see the difference between your German plant and your British plant read that notice." The German read the notice and nearly rolled over with laughter. "What's funny about that?" my annoyed British colleague said. "The German workers will do the same." It was pointed out that in the German plant an operator would expect to be fired if caught and that would be the end of the matter. In the UK plant it was clear that an operator had been caught and fired. This had probably resulted in either a strike or an industrial tribunal. In either case the operator would have been reinstated. The reason for reinstatement would have been on the basis that the operator concerned had not been warned in writing. Not only would the operator have been reinstated he would, in all probability, have been awarded damages for not having been given the requisite number of appropriate verbal and written warnings as specified in the company HR procedures. The award would probably have been enhanced to compensate for the hurt feelings and stress suffered by the operator concerned. To avoid the need to warn all operators in writing it clearly had been considered more cost effective and practical to put up the aforementioned notice for all to see.

What about the supervisor who caught and fired the operator? The reader may rest assured that he would have been given an appropriate written warning from the HR Department for having broken company procedures. His hurt feelings and stress suffered would probably have resulted in him letting the operators do as they please.

There is more to toilets, or the lack of them, than one might think.

THE NIGHT SHIFT
(How many jobs do your workforce have?)

For anybody who has never worked on a night shift, I would recommend that they do, if only to experience the feeling at 4 o'clock in the morning.

Continuous processing plants along with some batch processing and manufacturing plants that use expensive equipment run 24 hours per day in order to fully utilise their assets. There are various options in running a 24-hour operation. In all instances staff support services that are readily available during normal daytime hours, are unavailable, in spite of special callout arrangements that may have been made.

Given the choice, why would anyone wish to work nights on a permanent basis?

The obvious answer that springs to mind is that the pay is greater. The night shift is regarded as anti-social and attracts a premium allowance as a result.

There are however other opportunities that become available and need to be considered.

In the late 1960s I occupied the role of a Project and Development Engineer in a large American multi-national company that had acquired a large factory situated within sight of Edinburgh Castle, Scotland. The company had sold the site, which consisted of three distinct areas. Each area was separated by two major roads underneath which ran two large service tunnels connecting all three areas. The phased closure of the site meant that there was immediate access to an almost infinite variety of engineering machines and components that could either be used or modified to create machinery, that could be used to improve productivity in the area that was to be closed two years hence. No paperwork or approvals were required, which meant no procrastination. I was given a small team and we in effect became a small self-contained department within the company where the only pressure on us was to come up with results. We had no major problems with equipment that improved working conditions for the operators or those that improved productivity, provided nobody was made redundant.

Our pride and joy however was a different matter. This machine and ancillaries, which had taken considerable ingenuity on our part, would, if duplicated and implemented have resulted in job losses. This was immediately apparent to all who saw it when demonstrated in action on the shop floor. Prolonged negotiations concerning its use took place. The result was deadlock and our pride and joy was pushed on one side to gather cobwebs. I noticed after a while that there were subtle changes in the position of the machine, and that it had not acquired cobwebs, nor dust for that matter. 'It must be the night shift,' I thought, and resolved to find out. One very early morning my bleary eyes were opened wide when I turned up at work to see our pride and joy being used. The operators, whose work was now being done by 'our machine', were in the canteen, reading, playing cards and sleeping.

In 1979 I became the Manufacturing Manager of a company, which operated a night shift. I asked my predecessor whether he had experienced any problems with the night shift. "Funny you should ask that," he said, "I recently came back from London late at night, and, upon my return, saw a notice prominently displayed, offering a taxi service with a familiar looking phone number. I needed a taxi, rang the number, waited for it to appear, and when it did, I found myself looking at my night shift supervisor."

When in a position to do something about these matters, I made the occasional unannounced night shift visit. Some of the malpractices uncovered included:

˙ Clocking on and off of operators not on the premises.

Clocking on and off of family relatives, on the payroll, who were never there.

Trysts, being kept in the car park.

Sleeping on the premises.

The canteen used as a card school.

The hiding and storing of valuable metals such as lead and copper, that could later be sold.

Re-setting of automatic machines with the objective of enabling the operators to participate in some of the above.

It might interest the reader to note that when I fired someone as a result of some of the above, flagrantly bypassing written procedures in doing so, the only problems I encountered were from the HR Department. The shop floor attitude was invariably 'they had it coming' or, 'it should have happened sooner'. The person fired would invariably wish the issue to be kept quiet.

To those readers who may think that such behaviour could never possibly happen in their own organisations, I would suggest they consider the international scandal associated with British Nuclear Fuels Ltd. exposed in 1999 by the Japanese.

One should occasionally get up early, and look at what goes on in the night shift of your own organisation.

I would hate the reader to leave this chapter without learning some positive lessons. They include the following:

The best time to introduce manpower saving innovations is when the company is expanding, not contracting.

The workforce will grasp any opportunity that makes their job easier.

Employing supervisors, who, or whose family live in the same community as the workforce needs to be very, very, carefully considered.

Any loophole in procedures that can be exploited will be exploited.

There are always loopholes in procedures.

Your operators will find ways of increasing productivity, but not necessarily for the company's benefit.

One simple solution, often taken to avoid all the above and other bureaucratic hassle, is to start again, overseas. This approach of course could be considered a cop-out.

THE FACTORY INSPECTOR
(Saved by the hurricane of 1987?)

The Factory Inspectorate who celebrated their 150th anniversary in 1983 had legal powers to ensure that factories complied with safety regulation regarding the workplace. Companies had, and still have legal obligations regarding the safety of their workers. During my career I discussed many issues with Factory Inspectors some of which were related to a specific item of equipment, others of a more general nature.

An issue of a general nature that concerned the Area Factory Inspector with the company, for whom I was the Manufacturing Director, was that of fumes. The fumes were emitted as hot rubber products were removed from their machines. The company had many such machines. The fume extraction system, in the main, consisted of fans suspended from the factory roof. The Factory Inspector considered the system inadequate. The issue of fume extraction was persisted with and examples were quoted of what had been done elsewhere. My protestations that the workers smoked, and that money would be better spent on other items began to wear a little thin because, in the final analysis the company had a moral responsibility for the welfare of the workforce and a more efficient fume extraction system could have been installed.

On one of our walks around the factory, the Factory Inspector noticed a product that was designed for protecting the user in the event of chemical or nuclear warfare.

I was surprised that the Factory Inspector recognised the product and said so. It transpired that the Factory Inspector was a member of the local Territorial Army and had an allotted space in a nuclear fallout shelter. A very interesting discussion then ensued in my office concerning who had moral responsibility for whom. Did my workers have allotted places in fallout shelters? I certainly knew that I didn't. Switzerland had allotted spaces in nuclear fallout shelters for all its citizens, never mind a chosen few. It was clear that our Government considered that it had better things to spend money on, just like our company. Wasn't there a modicum of hypocrisy in our discussions? I argued.

Two months later one of our two factories had half its roof blown away as a result of the great storm that hit the south of England on October 15, 1987. The factory received a visit from the Factory Inspector shortly afterwards, and, noticing half the roof missing, said to me:

"I take it that this is your idea of dealing with the fume issue."

BLAME
(Anyone not here?)

At work and elsewhere it seems to be assumed that a problem will go away if someone can be blamed.

One day in the 1980s, a customer met our Chairman and Chief Executive Officer (CEO) at Heathrow Airport and took the opportunity to complain about the quality of one of his companies' products. I was the Manufacturing Director of the company that made that product. The net result was that our Managing Director (MD) was phoned on a Friday afternoon, and informed, in no uncertain manner, that this disgraceful state of affairs was an affront to the good name of the parent company, and that he was to attend a meeting forthwith at Head Office to resolve the matter. He was instructed to bring with him the Technical Director, the Quality Control Manager and the Chemist responsible for formulations. It was with considerable foreboding that the group set off. The Technical Director informed his wife that he suspected he would lose his job.

When the group returned I wasted no time in seeing the MD to ask how the meeting had gone on.

"It went better than I expected," said the MD. "We all blamed you." He then informed me that we both had to produce reports and that my report was to be on the subject of 'Production Control'. The reports had to be on the desk of the CEO at Head Office first thing Monday morning.

Shortly afterwards, our company had a visit from the CEO. At dinner the CEO informed me that he had read my report and enquired if I played golf. I answered affirmatively. The CEO then asked me whether or not I had been invited to the annual group golf outing at Wentworth. Upon being told not, he then told me to make arrangements with his secretary. I assumed that this would all be forgotten and didn't bother. A few days before the event I received a direct phone call from the CEO who said something along the lines, "I see you have not contacted my secretary, get it done now."

I have forgotten the contents of the report, but I can assure the reader that it didn't contain phrases such as:

"Our procedures will be looked at and lessons learned."

"Our management structure and responsibilities will be reviewed."

"Those responsible will be re-trained in order to meet expectations."

I suspect that had the report contained such, and similar phrases, I would not have been invited to play golf at Wentworth.

Nowadays, blame still appears to be regarded as a solution but the means of avoiding it appear to have changed.

WE CARE FOR OUR EMPLOYEES
(Do your employees think the same?)

In the 1980s I was the Manufacturing Director of a company that operated from two sites. The company was part of an engineering conglomerate.

One day I committed myself to an appointment with a member of the Civil Service who wished to know whether or not our company met statutory obligations by employing the requisite number of disabled personnel. During the discussion that followed, it was interesting to be informed that existing legislation instructed that all manned lifts had to be operated by disabled personnel. It was even more interesting to be informed that if every company in the UK wished to comply with the legislation there were insufficient disabled people available. At the end of the meeting however, it was apparent that we far exceeded legislative requirements, and the civil servant informed me that he would recommend our company for the 'Fit for Work' national award.

A few weeks later, to my surprise, I found out that our company had won this prestigious award. The result was that I was invited to Whitehall along with other fellow recipients. I was also asked to choose someone to present the award to our company. I choose the Lord Lieutenant of Kent. The Lord Lieutenant of Kent subsequently presented the award to our company in a local hotel. Resplendent in his official uniform, the Lord Lieutenant of Kent, an ex-governor of the Bank of England, did the occasion proud to the satisfaction of all those present. The guests included company employees and representatives of the local Civil Service amongst others.

Shortly afterwards, late one afternoon, I received a phone call from a local radio station asking would I, at short notice, be available to answer a few questions concerning our award, that would be asked by a DJ on his programme. I agreed, told nobody, and drove to the appointment, which took 15 minutes. I arrived at the address I was given, which was in one of the many rooms of a large office block near the local town centre. There were two desks, one of which was occupied by a man wearing earphones listening to what I assumed was the radio. He indicated to me to sit at an adjacent desk and put on the earphones lying on it. When it was indicated to me that I was on air, I recall answering the questions asked of me with a straight bat, so to speak. After completing this interesting side-show I decided to return to the factory and see how the late shift were getting on prior to the start of the night shift.

Walking down one of the gangways, I noticed one of our employees rushing towards me, his face purple with rage, mouthing a variety of expletives. Taken aback by this surprisingly, out of character behaviour, I asked the operator concerned what the problem was.

"Was that you on the radio?" he asked.

"Yes," I replied.

"It's an absolute disgrace," he said, and continued, "You never told them there was nothing wrong with us before we started working here, did you?"

I don't recall assuring that particular operator that we cared for our employees.

REDUNDANCY
(Why me? Why not?)

Organisations wax and wane. In addition to survival one would hope fairness and justice would be the prevalent aim when organisations need to reduce the numbers of their employees. Employment legislation is in force with the aim of ensuring that this is so. There are however many questions posed on the issue of redundancy amongst which include the following:

How are the numbers to be reduced decided upon?

Are the decisions best made at local level or Head Office?

How are the individuals concerned picked?

In 1980 I was the Manufacturing Director of a small rubber manufacturing company that was part of an expanding conglomerate. Our company had two factories and employed approximately 150 personnel. UK industry at that time was in the throes of an economic squeeze, orders were falling and it was clear that cutbacks of personnel would be necessary. In compliance with legislation, I addressed the workforce, explained the situation and gave notice that redundancies were inevitable. I had, in my mind, decided upon the number of personnel that could be reduced without damaging our manufacturing capability, and wished to implement the required action as soon as possible. Upon discussing the situation with the Managing Director I was surprised to be told that we should do nothing until told to by Head Office. The reason for this was that reductions would only be considered relevant from the date we were told by Head

Office. Reductions made before that date would not be considered as part of the reduction plan.

The MD was subsequently summoned to Head Office and was told the numbers to be reduced. On being told the numbers, the issue remained as to who should be chosen. The Managing Director, an accountant, wished to minimise costs and wanted to remove those who would involve the least cost to the company, basically last in first out. I wished to remove those who I considered least productive at the workplace. The Union Shop Steward whilst not wanting any reductions would have preferred a voluntary system supplemented by last in first out. The individual workers wanted to know whether they themselves were on the list and pestered me at every available opportunity.

In order to avoid leakage from within the company the Managing Director and myself decided that the best place to resolve our differences would be for the pair of us to resolve the issue at one of our houses. My house was chosen as it was nearest to the plants.

The issue was discussed in detail in the front room of my house. My wife, who having served tea and biscuits retired to sit in one corner of the room, switched on the TV and left the two of us to finalise our business. When we finally agreed on who was to be made redundant the Managing Director stood up from the sofa, stretched himself, and said, "One thing puzzles me, when the Group Chief Executive told me the numbers to be reduced he didn't have his black book with him in which he normally makes his notes, and yet he remembered, because he repeated the number when he rang me only this week to check on how we were progressing." After pausing he then asked me, "How did he remember that number?"

Whilst we both looked at each other, my wife turned around from watching the TV and said, "It would have been the date on which you had your meeting at Head Office." The MD paused, turned, stared at me again, and said, "Good grief she is right."

It may seem to the reader that this method is somewhat unscientific, and more sensitive souls may suggest that the meeting should have been postponed to the first week of the following month in order that the numbers were minimised. In any event this method would clearly not suffice for companies employing thousands. The reader may suspect, correctly, that I did not consider offering myself to be one of the names on my list, and may wonder how the issue of making large reductions in Head Office is made.

A method used by the same Chief Executive Officer concerned a company that had been acquired by the conglomerate. The company manufactured a product that was in demand, but the profits made by the company were considered inadequate. At the first meeting with the Chief Executive Officer, the Managing Director of the company was told in effect that his company made a good product but to reach the required profit level all that was required was a reduction of 50% of the office staff. The Managing Director was then tasked to implement the required reductions.

At the next meeting, held one month later, the Chief Executive asked what progress had been made. The Managing Director then explained that there had been none, and proceeded to explain why all the members of his staff were needed for the well-being of the company. The Chief Executive then said, "I believe you need help, bring your Human Resources Director with you and follow me."

The Chief Executive proceeded to take the Managing Director to one end of the Main Office, stood in the centre and then said, "This is how you reduce your staff by 50%, I want everybody on the right hand side of the office off the premises within the next two hours, or there will be a new Managing Director."

Some years later towards the end of my career I was tasked to pick up the Chief Executive of an international company who I knew had been a Director of one of the many companies comprising the aforementioned conglomerate. The subject of the Chief Executive Officer arose, and I told the above story based on hearsay. I was then told, "That was not the end of it. The Managing Director concerned was horrified on being told what to do and said that his office was on the right. The CEO then told the MD that if that was so he had twenty minutes to move his office to the left hand side.

Readers may find the above somewhat brutal and arbitrary, which of course it is. There are some redeeming features to this tale. It did produce results. There was no procrastination.

Imagine the victims subsequently interviewed for a new job being asked to explain why they had left the company, saying truthfully, "I was fired because my desk was situated on the right hand side of the main office." The obvious flaw to this is that it would probably not be believed. The Human Resources Department would probably enquire as to whether it was stated in the company written procedures that staff redundancies would be made by choosing those sitting on the right hand side of the main office. The only fair method would be to toss a coin to decide right or left hand side.

It can be seen from the above examples that instructions from head office do not involve any knowledge of the human situation at the plant level. Accusations of prejudice and unfair treatment against individuals would be difficult to prove. Decisions made at local level on the other hand are fraught with difficulties in this respect. One can imagine some members of the legal profession salivating at the opportunities available in the event of anyone suing a company for unfair dismissal.

It does not take too much imagination to picture the following question (Q) and answer (A) dialogue at an Industrial Tribunal hearing:

Q1. "You say that my client is not up to the job? Answer, Yes or No."

A1. "Yes."

Q2/3/4. "Have you written evidence stating this? Why have you not trained my client to your required standards? I put it to you that my client is a victim of your managerial incompetence and that you have been derelict in your duties. How do you answer? Yes or No."

A2. "I meant to say No to the first question."

Q5. "Ah, so you now admit that my client was up to the job, it is quite clear that my client has been victimised and as such, in view of the situation my client is now in, I suggest that a substantial monetary payment should be made, well in excess of the measly pittance given in your redundancy payment plan. My client has suffered a nervous breakdown, the marital relationship is in tatters, in addition to which my client feels inadequate and cannot face neighbours and friends, other than the Doctor. In short my client's life has been ruined. What do you say to that? Answer Yes or No."

A3. "I'm not going to answer on the grounds that I may incriminate myself."

To avoid the above scenario and the potentially prohibitive costs involved in Industrial Tribunals, two-thirds of claims are settled out of court. 'No-win, no-fee' lawyers exploit the system to win handsome payments without even entering the court. It is easy and costs nothing for an employee to cook up a claim. The 'service industry' involved is basically legalised extortion.

Another management approach is to use Management Consultants, brought in under the pretext of effecting improvements to the operations within the plant concerned.

They, as outsiders, cannot possibly be accused of bias. Those who use Management Consultants if lucky, have time to reflect upon the definition of Management Consultants, given by Robert Townsend in his book *Up the Organisation*, namely:

'Management Consultants will borrow your watch to tell you the time, and, after having done so, proceed to walk off with the watch.'

What at first may seem a simple task of reducing numbers within an organisation can be fraught with difficulties. This is especially so if the organisation operates within a country where legislation has encouraged the growth of service industries who thrive on feeding off manufacturing industries.

It is not surprising that countless UK manufacturing industries have ended up as corpses.

PRODUCTIVITY
(Does it go up in smoke?)

The issue of our poor national productivity performance compared with those who we regard as our industrial competitors such as the USA, Japan, Germany and France, has always been an issue that has tasked our Government since the First World War. Many Government papers, books and newspaper articles have been written on the subject.

It came as a surprise to many that during the 1974 three day working week, brought about by the Miners' Strike, that national output remained virtually unchanged from when the country worked a normal five or six day week. Many thought that this was due to our fighting bulldog approach that could always be relied upon in times of adversity. Some people however, concluded that it gave a simple measure of our national efficiency, and wondered how the country could spend two to three days at work basically doing nothing.

In the early 1980s 1 was a Manufacturing Director responsible for the output and the meeting of deadlines for a multitude of different products being produced by a mixed labour force. I was aware that the majority of the workforce smoked. One had only to walk around the factory perimeter and plough through mountains of cigarette butts situated at certain points. At the time my wife was a heavy smoker and, as a non-smoker myself, I noticed that my wife had a cigarette at least every half hour. For a smoker, two breaks during a working day are clearly insufficient to suit their needs. Hanging up no-smoking signs will not solve the problem either. I could not be bothered to find or chase workers from their smoking spots, so one day I assembled them all together and explained that I didn't wish to find them away from their workplace smoking, and suggested that they smoke anytime they wished, at their place of work, provided that they dropped their cigarette butt ends in appropriate receptacles that would be provided. I might add that, as a weedy looking non-smoker, I did point out that smoking was bad for their health. The workforce wholeheartedly agreed with the proposal, and it was implemented.

A few weeks later I compared production figures both prior to, and after the proposal was implemented. The change had resulted in an increase in output averaging 15%. In short, allowing the workforce to smoke at their place of work had resulted in a permanent increase in production of 15%. A further benefit was that the workforce thought I was a decent chap as far as managers were concerned.

A few years later I was the Engineering Director of a much larger company, attending a board meeting when the topic of poor productivity was raised. I suggested the above, relating my experience.

"We can't have that here," said the Human Resources Director. "We have a non smoking policy." Considerable discussion then took place, the issue was put to a vote and the proposal was rejected by a vote four to two. The two were the Production Director and myself. The four other directors took what they considered was the high moral ground. They of course, did not consider themselves responsible for productivity.

BONUS ALLOCATION
(Any other opportunities?)

During the 1980s our group company introduced a bonus scheme for the companies within the group. The scheme applied to senior members of staff only.

The scheme was based on audited year end budgeted profits. Profits above budget would receive proportionally increased bonuses up to a certain limit.

Our company supplied many products to other companies within the group. One particular product was hand built and expensive, and as such, it would often be the subject of disputes concerning quality standards. The standard procedure in such a dispute would be that the product would be returned from the customer, accompanied with an appropriate debit note. The end result would be a reconciliation process held at the end of the financial year whereby invoices from our company and debits raised by our customer would be resolved in order that the accounts could be closed. Our Managing Director in conjunction with our Financial Director always did the reconciliation negotiations with the customer's Financial Director.

It had been noticed by us, but not by our customer, that an individual product that had been rejected on one occasion would be acceptable on another occasion. There were various reasons for this, which meant in practice that an individual product could accumulate more than one debit note and associated invoice. The net result was that at the year end there was often considerable money at stake for both companies, dependant on how the invoice and debit note issue was resolved. The issue was normally settled on a 50:50 basis, which the reader will appreciate would be to our company's advantage in that we had invariably supplied some of the products on more than one occasion.

At the end of the financial year following the inauguration of the bonus system, our customer's Financial Director was busy celebrating the bonus performance with his co-Directors and delegated the reconciliation negotiation to a senior member of his staff who was not on the bonus scheme. The reconciliation split that year ended up 100:0 in our favour.

Two lessons learned from this little episode are that weaknesses in your procedural systems will be exploited, and that the delegation of money matters is sometimes, if not always, a mistake.

The main lesson learned however, is that bonus allocation causes discontent to those not receiving a bonus. This may seem obvious, but apparently those receiving such bonuses neither acknowledge nor seem aware of the discontent that bonuses cause.

RULES AND PROCEDURES
(Are they relevant and abided by?)

A common occurrence in the UK during the 1960s and 1970s was the experience of waiting on a railway platform for a British Rail train whose operators were 'working to rule'. Working to rule meant that the train would be late or not even arrive. The effects were often more pernicious than strikes. Working to rules and procedures were one of many practices employed during industrial disputes. On the basis that working to rules and procedures resulted in little or no work being done, then presumably working normally meant that rules and procedures were being broken on a continual basis.

From the amount of legislation that continues to be passed, it would appear that the Government perceive their constituents to be basically gormless, with behavioural patterns of feckless children. The Government may of course be correct in this view. Is it possible that management regard their workers in a similar manner?

In the 1990s I was in the process of hosting a factory tour with a Japanese VIP, when we reached a line of eight programmable machines, each of which inserted plastic pins at various intervals, producing products of various lengths. One operator controlled all eight machines. Our Japanese guest stopped by one of the machines, adjacent to the operator, and he picked up the Operational Check List (OCL), issued by the Technical Quality Assurance Department. With the OCL sheet in his hand, and with myself behind him, facing the operator, the following conversation took place between our Japanese guest and the operator:

"It says on this sheet that you must inspect this part after each 100 is produced," said our guest.

"Yes," replied the operator.

"Do you inspect every 100th part?"

"I do," said the operator.

"I did not see you counting them," said our guest politely.

'What will the response be?' I thought.

"Actually I don't count, I know that the machine produces this part every 36 seconds, so I pick up a part every hour and inspect it," said the machine operator.

'Excellent answer,' I thought, 'this operator is clearly no fool.'

"I see that you have no watch on your wrist, how do you know when each hour has passed?" said our guest ever so politely.

'This is getting serious,' I thought, 'how will the operator answer this one?'

"I don't need a watch, I look at that clock over there," said the operator pointing to a wall clock in the far distance.

Our Japanese guest bent down at the waist, straight legged, and swayed side to side. He looked in the direction of the clock, straightened himself up and said to the operator in an even more polite manner, "Very difficult to see is that clock."

As I walked away with our Japanese guest, I nodded approvingly to the operator thinking how smart he was. I also thought, at the same time, what a set of buffoons we, in management were, in regard to our rules and procedures. Both thoughts exactly what I suspected our Japanese guest wished me to think.

WAREHOUSES
(Do you know where they are and what is in them?)

Warehouses are generally perceived to be places for storing raw materials and for storing finished goods awaiting dispatch. The manner, and system by which goods are stored and moved in and out of a warehouse invariably gives a good indication of the effectiveness of the factory.

Warehouses are also places where the 'dead bodies' of an organisation are often kept. Goods and materials that are liabilities can be stored and declared as assets. This practice comes to light when seemingly profitable companies collapse due to cash flow problems. The first place one should look at during any factory tour is the warehouse. Warehousing facilities are normally ignored in most factory visits. The exceptions are invariably Japanese visitors.

In the early 1990s, three of us had been invited to dinner at the home of our Japanese host who lived on the outskirts of Tokyo. We ordered a taxi from our hotel, and presented the address card that we had been given, to the taxi driver. The taxi driver took the card, bowed, and then took us on our way. During the trip, the taxi driver repeatedly stopped and showed passers-by the address card. It was very clear that the driver did not know how to arrive at our destination. The stoppages occurred so often that we commented amongst ourselves about what we perceived to be the taxi driver's incompetence.

A few months later I showed a Japanese VIP around our manufacturing facilities. Our Japanese guest spent a considerable amount of time in our warehouse asking very pertinent and probing questions. After the tour the whole management team assembled to listen to what our VIP Japanese visitor had to say.

Our visitor started his talk by saying that when he first came to the UK as a young man to Oxford, he was extremely impressed by our national address system.

"You obtain the address of the person you wish to visit, you obtain a map, you go to the town, you find the street, you walk along numbered houses, you knock on the appropriate numbered door and you meet the person you came to visit, assuming he or she was in. Very simple and effective is your UK address system, unlike our Japanese address system," he said.

At this point I sat up, vividly recalling my taxi trip in Japan, and waited for the punch line which I was sure would follow.

"I cannot understand why in the UK, your factories use the Japanese address system in your warehouses."

VAT
(Are you a smart Alec?)

VAT is basically a means of raising revenue for the Government imposed on business where business itself is responsible for the administration and payment. Ignoring illegal sophisticated scams that have taken advantage of claim back procedures, there would appear to be little opportunity to take advantage of the VAT system in order to increase profitability at the expense of one's own customers, or would there?

In the early 1980s I was the Company Engineering Director during an expansion phase that was required as a result of the company having become the sole supplier to a major UK automobile manufacturer. Part of the expansion included extending the company's IT capability, which involved the installation of cables in underground tunnels dug by a robotic mole. Whilst work was in progress I was informed one day that the mole had lost itself whilst burrowing underneath a road. This disclosure caused a few ribald comments. The contractor responsible had to bring a JCB excavator on site in order to find the mole. I commented to the Services Engineer concerned that this would result in additional costs to the contractor and that those costs would ultimately be passed on to our company. I was assured that this would not be possible, as the contractor was working to a fixed price as per their written quotation.

Two weeks later the JCB was still on site and I expressed my concern again, indicating how much the JCB itself would have cost to hire. I was again assured that my concerns were groundless, even though it was clear that the contractor would lose a considerable sum. The Services Engineer promised me that he would present me with the final invoice when it was received, along with the original quotation.

A few weeks later the final invoice and original quotation were presented to me with a comment to the effect that my concerns had been totally unnecessary. I thanked the Services Engineer, and pondered why the contractor did not appear to be unduly concerned with what was clearly a disastrous project from his viewpoint. I sat down and compared the quotation with the final invoice. The quotation price, as one would expect, showed a cost to which was added VAT. The invoice consisted of the quotation price to which VAT had again been added. In essence, VAT had been added twice. With VAT at 15%, the contractor's invoice was 17.5% higher than his quotation price. 'Very interesting', I thought, and went to the Accounts Department to check on other previous invoices and quotations from the same contractor. The invoices and quotations that I looked at all followed the same pattern of sharp practice. The contractor in effect was submitting and being paid invoices that were 17.5% higher than the quotations. Intrigued by what I had discovered, I then checked other contractor's quotations and invoices and found that many of them performed the same sharp practice. The company, over time, had lost thousands of pounds and would have continued to do so unless the Accounts Department changed their checking procedures.

I thought at the time that the disclosure would enhance my career. I wrote to the other Directors, sorted out the contractors under my control and waited to see what developments occurred, especially from the Accounts Department.

The reader might like to know that the main lesson I learned from this tale was:

'Nobody likes a smart Alec, especially one who treads on other people's toes.'

SUPPLIER QUALITY IMPROVEMENT
(Are public show trials the answer?)

As a student, taking some interest in politics, I was intrigued how so many students were attracted to a system whereby people accused of unbelievable, ludicrous and outrageous crimes would plead guilty, knowing that they would be shot as a result. Reading *Darkness at Noon,* by Arthur Koestler, did provide some insight.

In the late 1960s as the Plant Mechanical Engineer of a continuous process plant producing synthetic rubber bales for tyre manufacturers, I recall observing a hydraulic baling machine in order to see if there was an obvious solution to persistent intermittent problems that kept occurring. The machine converted continuously fed rubber flakes into bales of rubber. The bales were supplied to different tyre companies. I noticed that considerable quantities of rubber flakes missed the mouth of the baling machine and ended up on the floor. The plant operator, who was also tasked with keeping his area clean consequently swept the floor and to my surprise deposited the contents into the mouth of the baling machine.

"Do we get complaints from our customers," I asked.

"No, but we don't sweep up whilst making bales for customer X," he replied.

"Why only Customer X," I naïvely asked.

"Because they are the only customer that inspect incoming goods," he replied.

It was no surprise whose tyres I bought the next time my car had its tyres changed.

Inspecting customer incoming goods is all very well, you might think, but what happens if the customer operates 'just in time' (JIT) techniques, such as in a modern car plant?

In the 1990s I was the Manufacturing Director of a plant that supplied parts to various car manufacturers, which included a well-known American automotive company and a well-known Japanese automotive company.

As one can imagine, the top priority supplying a car assembly track is to ensure that the customer does not run out of your product. The penalty for causing a car track stoppage was extremely stressful for any supplier concerned. In ensuring continuous supply, what might seem a minor problem to the supplier could be a major problem to the customer. An example of this would be if right hand parts were placed in a box marked for left hand parts.

One day I read in a trade journal that the American Car Company was experiencing problems with its UK suppliers and that a top Quality Control executive would be dispatched from the USA to sort them all out. As a UK supplier, the Managing Director and myself were eventually summoned to attend the appropriate meeting. We left our plant in the evening, stayed overnight in a hotel, and arrived promptly on our customers' site early the following morning.

The meeting consisted of listening to threats accompanied with appropriate American expletives and much fist banging on the desk. It was clear to us during the harangue that the gentleman concerned not only did not know who our company was, but was also not familiar with our product. I recall leaving that car plant with a certain amount of anger, having to my mind, wasted a whole day.

One day our Japanese Marketing Director received a call from our associate supplier in Japan, informing him that our common Japanese customer was experiencing problems with us.

As a result of these concerns the caller said that the Marketing Director, the Quality Control Manager and myself, the Manufacturing Director, would be required to attend a meeting to present a report. The meeting was to be held four weeks later on the premises of our Japanese customer. Upon being informed, I had a report ready two weeks later, well ahead of the scheduled meeting. The report had taken me approximately two hours to compose and write.

One week before the meeting, we had a visit from our Japanese associate supplier who had come to see how we were progressing with our reports. I was quite pleased that I had completed my report, and, aware that my colleagues had not done their reports, gave him my copy feeling rather smug. My report was politely placed on one side and the three of us were informed that we should, on an immediate basis, delegate our duties for the duration of a week, the time which he considered would be required to produce a report worthy of being received by our customer. My smugness had now deserted me and I recall thinking, 'a week, what a waste of time, he has got to be joking'. However, familiar with the way things were done in Japan, I knew that this was not the case.

The report, guided by our Japanese associate, started with the drawing of a large 'Cause and Effect' (Fishbone or Ishikawa) diagram, where we had to complete under major cause headings, (bones), sub causes (smaller bones), contributing answers to the effect or problem, (fish head) titled:

'Why we displease – X' (our customer).

A week later we presented our report at the premises of our customer, to an audience that comprised of our customers' staff and workforce. I recall leaving that car plant feeling rather uncomfortable, perplexed, and having a peculiar feeling of having let our customer down. The whole episode took over a week.

I often reflected upon the effectiveness of the two different approaches, that of the American company, and that of the Japanese company. I recall in particular thinking in the latter case, that I had received a very slight inkling and a practical insight of how victims of political show trials must have felt.

SEEING OURSELVES AS OTHERS SEE US
(Inselaffen?)

It has always puzzled me that the person I see in the mirror is not the person that my wife sees.

One day in 1996 whilst at work in a German car plant, my bi-lingual colleague passed some remarks, which included the phrase, 'those bloody Krauts'. Rather than reprimanding him concerning his politically incorrect remark I pointed out that it wasn't much of an insult, and asked him what derogatory name did the Germans have for the British. He told me that he didn't know, which rather surprised me, as I knew that he had spent considerable time as a student in Germany. I then tasked him to find out, whilst performing his normal duties, and let me know the answer.

Two or three weeks later he came to me grinning, and said that he had found the answer. He told me that the Germans called us, the British, 'Inselaffen'. He had overheard a conversation during which a German supervisor was commenting to a German colleague about 'that Inselaffe', who happened to be English. (I might add that, contrary to what our national parties might think, the Germans didn't distinguish between the Scots, the Welsh or the English). 'What does 'Inselaffe' and 'Inselaffen' mean?' I, and another colleague asked. 'Island ape, Island apes', was the reply. The three of us were highly amused to the extent that we were still laughing about it later in the evening at our hotel across the border in Luxembourg. The hotel proprietor, who knew us quite well, enquired what was amusing us. Upon being told she recoiled back in horror, and said, 'but zat ees an eensult'. Our explanation that we knew it was an insult, but an extremely perceptive and incisive one, did not appear to reassure her.

The following day I mentioned to my German counterpart, about our newly discovered knowledge. "Is that so?" was his thoughtful response, and he then changed the topic.

Three months later, in the EUFA European Football Championship (Euro 96) quarter-finals, England beat Spain 4-2 on penalties. England's next opponents, in the semi-finals at Wembley were Germany.

I was at my desk in the UK when I received a phone call from my German counterpart. I was informed that he wished to send me a fax that only I, and nobody else should see. He insisted that I should be by the side of the designated fax machine when it was despatched. I lifted the fax directly after it had chattered through the machine and found myself staring at a sketch. The sketch showed a Union Jack coated gorilla, leaning against a football goalpost with one arm, with a football tucked underneath the other arm. Underneath the sketch was the caption: 'Waiting for Germany'

Shortly afterwards I received a phone call from my German counterpart who enquired, "Did I get it?"

For those readers not aware of the result of that semi final, England lost to Germany 6-5 on penalties, and Germany went on to beat the Czech Republic 2-1 in the final.

Section C

CONCEPTS REGARDING WORK

'The bad workmen who form the majority of the operatives in many branches of industry are decidedly of the opinion that bad workmen ought to receive the same wages as good.'

John Stuart Mill
1806-1873

C1

WAGE NEGOTIATIONS
(Concluded in Downing Street?)

In our current society, most businesses exist to make a legal profit. Management are expected to perform this task by reconciling the conflicting interests of shareholders, customers and the workforce, the latter for whom it has a legal responsibility.

Unions came into existence because workers were often exploited and believed that under the capitalist system they would never get their fair share of the profits made by the business. In short the reconciliation as such was perceived by them to be to their disadvantage.

Following the Second World War, it was thought by some, that the nationalisation of industries, created for the benefit of society as a whole, would have resulted in no strikes, because there would be no profit allocation to a perceived few greedy capitalist shareholders. The reality was considerably different, and the UK eventually became accustomed to seeing strikes by the NUM, AEU, TGWU and the NUR, amongst others, settled in Downing Street, over beer and sandwiches. (So we were led to believe at the time.) The belief that unions were more powerful than the Government was strengthened when the then head of the TGWU, Frank Cousins, preferred his position in the union to that of a Government Cabinet Minister.

The above negotiation scenario was played out on a smaller scale throughout the factories of the UK in the 1960s and 1970s.

During my formative career I witnessed many supervisors and managers broken by recalcitrant shop stewards.

As a graduate engineer in a manufacturing environment it was, and still is, essential to obtain management responsibilities in order to become a Chartered Engineer. In consideration of this I took management roles whenever the opportunity arose. In these roles, in view of my previous observations, I would always ensure that the workers knew who I was by talking to them directly about their work, during regular walkabouts. I would always go out of my way to try and get to know the shop stewards.

The opportunity to get involved directly in wage negotiations first came when I became Manufacturing Manager of a company that was part of a relatively small but growing conglomerate. The year prior to my recruitment, the company had had a strike, which had eventually been settled by the full time Union Area Representative.

When wage negotiations commenced there was, compared to the previous year, a new Managing Director, a new shop steward, the previous shop steward and myself. With a clean sheet, so to speak, we, from the outset, explained to the shop stewards that we had no intention of allowing our negotiations to proceed beyond the factory level. We explained that this was because we did not want their Area Representative, and the subsequent involvement of our Human Resources (HR) Director from HQ, meddling in our affairs, and then walking off without having to deal with the consequences.

When negotiations reached the point at which we said was our final offer, the shop stewards submitted our offer to the workforce for approval. As anticipated, the offer was rejected and the workforce demanded that the negotiations continue with the full time Union Representative. The workforce perceived that they had nothing to lose and everything to gain. We pointed out to the Stewards that the presence of their Area Representative would necessitate us having to bring in our equivalent, namely our HR Director from HQ. We also emphasised that in the event that we did concede to a new proposal, the workforce would see that our final offer was in fact a bluff. Much more to the point it would also show that they, the shop stewards, were not as capable as their full time representative, making them, the two stewards both irrelevant in the eyes of the workforce. Notwithstanding our logic, the stewards were unable to persuade the workforce and the negotiations proceeded to the next stage. We were in fact put under immense pressure to concede something both from the union and from our own HR Director from HQ. We stuck to our position by repeatedly telling 'our man' that in the event that we conceded, he, and not us would be responsible for any shortfalls in our budget. (The budget was regarded as sacrosanct.) To the Union Representative we said that we had no intention of being fired because we failed to meet our budget. We repeatedly informed him that his stewards had extracted everything possible and that they had done the union proud. Our final offer was in fact our final offer. Our stewards witnessed everything. Our final offer was finally accepted. There was no strike. The lesson learned by everybody at both factories was that events get out of hand when outsiders, whose interests are basically different, get involved. It was perceived by everybody 'on the inside' that things were best settled in-house. In short, wage negotiations are best settled in-house by those who have to live with the consequences of any agreements made.

The above situation contrasted strongly with my next company, where, after being 'head hunted' for the position as Engineering Director I expressed an interest in wage negotiations. Negotiations within the company traditionally involved the company HR Director, the Manufacturing Director and various shop stewards. Wage negotiations were held off site during normal working hours and were always eventually settled using the Union full time representative. The Company Managing Director was not directly involved in negotiations, and the HR Director did not have to deal with the consequences of any agreement made.

The big difference between the two companies was the existence of a company Human Resources Director in one company and none in the other. In the former company the Human Resources or Personnel Department had been fired as a result of a cost saving exercise. The role of the HR manager was incorporated into my job as Manufacturing Director and his secretary's role was given to a clerk in the wages department on the basis that she dealt with most of the queries, which invariably concerned wages. The idea of firing the whole of the personnel department had come from a book titled *Up The Organisation*, by Robert Townsend. A book I had read in the late 1960s.

The reader who may wonder why some organisations seem incapable of sorting out their own affairs without some form of outside intervention taking place, should consider that the self-interests of those involved in negotiations may conflict with the interests of the organisation itself. It may well seem strange that an organisation's own Human Resources Department may well be one of them.

MANAGEMENT DEVELOPMENT
(Inter-company movement? Are you joking?)

In the early 1980s the British engineering conglomerate to which our company belonged, acquired a company larger than ourselves and to whom we were suppliers.

Our Head Office Human Resource (HR) Director was tasked to show the newly acquired company HR Director around the various company plants and facilities of the conglomerate which his company was now part of. Our company was one of the companies that were visited.

On arrival at our company, the new HR director, as one might expect, was not interested in the facilities, but more in the people within them, and, as such I found myself as Manufacturing Director, being asked to join the two of them in our Managing Director's office. The ensuing conversation and discussion touched upon various issues when the newcomer turned to the Head Office HR Director, commented upon the variety of companies now within the control of the parent company, and asked if, in view of the parent company's expanding size, whether there was a policy being considered for developing their managers.

"We have a very simple policy," said the Head Office HR Director.

"If someone is satisfactory at their job we don't see the point in moving them around. If they are unsatisfactory we fire them."

I suspected at the time that this response to a forward thinking HR question gave an insight as to why the larger company had been acquired and had not been the acquirer.

C3

OWNERSHIP
(Does it matter?)

In the late 1960s I bought my first house in Scotland. Most of my Scottish peers thought I was crazy because they said I would be saddled with debt for the rest of my life. Renting is better than ownership it was said to me.

Political parties vie with each other over the relative merits of state ownership versus private ownership. Companies compete with each other over the ownership of other companies, often at great expense to the companies themselves as they knowingly pay huge sums to the financiers and banks concerned. Ownership, it would appear, comes down to control. In simple terms if you are not the owner you have no control nor power.

During the 1990s, towards the twilight stages of my career, more than one German said to me, "You English don't seem to care who own your companies." I must admit that as an individual, I didn't care who the owner of my company was, provided that I was paid, but I certainly cared about who owned my house. The Germans it would appear didn't seem to care who owned their houses as long as they could live in one, but they certainly cared about who owned their companies.

There is more to ownership than one might think.

In the late 1960s, the American owned company I was working for, had sold the premises with the result that certain products had to be relocated. I, as a Project Engineer, familiar with those products, went to USA to look at best practice and to ensure from their viewpoint that I understood the costs that would result in the setting up of a new plant. During this visit I met the Chief Executive of Engineering. I returned to the UK where I became part of a small team evaluating sites and submitting proposals for approval. Our proposals were continually rejected. The team reached the stage when we believed time had run out.

I had in fact started to look around for another job.

One day, unexpectedly, I was summoned to go to Italy. The parent company had been in 'secret' negotiations with an Italian company for 50% ownership of a modern plant in Southern Italy. The company auditors had requested an engineer to value and technically assess the plant, as they had no means of evaluating it other than looking at the books.

'Was the equipment modern?' 'Were the processes involved, state of the art?' 'Was the plant as good as those being proposed in the USA?' 'Was the plant itself worth what the Italians said it was?' All questions amongst others that the parent company needed to know.

The Chief Executive of Engineering in USA whose staff at the time were fully occupied with relocation projects in USA, when asked to supply an engineer, must have remembered me, that British engineer.

Some short time later I found myself in Milan where I met the company auditors.

The auditor's offices had once been the home of the Italian opera composer Verdi.

The office rooms had beautiful double doors that closed in on each other, creating a soundproof environment. The rooms themselves had beautiful paintings on the walls and ceilings. 'I am in the wrong job,' I thought at the time.

I was eventually taken to the new plant, which was situated in the outskirts of a beautiful Roman-medieval town, a few miles inland from the Adriatic resort of San Benedetto del Tronto.

When I had compiled my detailed report, I, along with a representative of the auditors presented my report, in Milan, to the Italian company representative who was the Plant Director, an Engineer (Dott. Ing.) He expressed total satisfaction with the report. The report had to satisfy four parties. Firstly, the company I worked for, who needed reassurance that the plant was as good as anything they were doing in USA but at less cost. Secondly, the Italian company, who having built the plant with a combination of their own and state money would, end up owning half a company for little, nothing, or even a surplus, depending on the report's valuation. Thirdly were the auditors, who would wish to continue doing business with the company and fourthly, myself, who wanted to keep his job.

Just before the deal was finalised I showed the USA Chief Executive of Engineering around the new plant in the south of Italy. I have forgotten the many questions he asked except for one, which was repeated on more than one occasion:

"Are you sure that they (the Italians), *own* this lot?"

The significance of the question did not hit home until years later, when, in 1993 I found myself intrigued by the headline news that Ferranti, a hugely successful British company was in receivership.

I first became aware of Ferranti as a student. In 1964 it was the subject of heated student political arguments that revolved around the fact that it had been severely penalised by the Government of the day for making excess profits supplying the Bloodhound missile. The Bloodhound missile was an extremely successful missile and was exported to other countries. Similar companies that were working on and supplying missiles that didn't work, were not penalised, as they were not making excess profits. It was apparently OK to provide the UK Government of the day with rubbish provided you didn't make excess profits. Excess profit was regarded as exploitation, up with which the

Government and taxpayer would not put. (I apologise for the misquotation.)

Ferranti was part nationalised in 1975. The Government shares were then sold to City Institutions in 1980.

In 1982, the last Ferranti Chairman, was succeeded by a City appointee.

In 1987, in the pursuit of growth, Ferranti purchased an American company named International Signal & Control. (ISC). The joint company was named Ferranti International Ltd.

In 1989 Ferranti in the UK discovered that it had overvalued ISC by £215million.

The founder of ISC and co-chairman of Ferranti International Ltd, John Gueren, admitted to an American court that he was guilty of a $1.14 billion fraud and a $50 million smuggling ring. He was sentenced to 15 years' imprisonment.

Ferranti, from being a leading force in the global defence industry with a market value of £1 billion, employing a workforce of 26,000 had in the space of five years been reduced to bankruptcy with shares suspended at 1p per share and 90% of its workers gone.

It would appear that one needs to know who owns what and what is owned, and that due diligence might not help in this matter.

On a personal level, as I was getting older I thought it would be a good idea to supplement my pension contributions by purchasing PEPs (now ISAs), on an annual basis whenever circumstances allowed it. One such PEP consisted solely of Railtrack shares. I was aware at the time that the opposition of the day were opposed to the privatisation of British Rail. I was surprised that privatisation did not result in reverting back to the old LMS, LNER and GWR arrangement that had served the country well throughout two World Wars. I was also aware, having an engineering mindset, that the separation of the track from those using it would result in a moneymaking opportunity for the legal profession in that fines for lateness, imposed by the rail regulator on the train owners, would be recovered if they blamed and sued the track owner, which was Railtrack. Railtrack in turn would clearly be better off, from a financial aspect, subcontracting all maintenance work so that it too could sue its own subcontractors. Summarising, as a result of the manner of privatisation, the logical policy for Railtrack was to fire its own maintenance workers and replace them with lawyers.

In spite of these considerations I thought the ownership of Railtrack shares could not go wrong because of the total assets owned by Railtrack.

One day, I was driving my car along with my wife going to play golf, when it was announced on the car radio that Railtrack had in effect been taken back under Government control. "Did you hear that, you've lost our money," said my wife. "Don't worry," I replied. "We will get our money back because Railtrack own all those assets."

In case the reader is getting a little confused a recap of the situation is worthwhile.

The UK Government, which owned British Rail on behalf of the tax paying public, had taken more money off some of the public in exchange for shares in order that they could become shareholders, or owners, of a smaller portion (Railtrack) of the larger company (British Rail).

Following a series of railway track maintenance disasters, the opposition who had now become the Government decided that, for the benefit of the public, it would remove control from the shareholders and change the name of Railtrack to Network Rail. Network Rail would become a not for profit company without shareholders.

One obvious solution for the problems created by Railtrack would have been to fire the Board of Directors. The Government action taken, however, served many political purposes, one of which was the avoidance of the need to pay compensation to Railtrack shareholders, the legal owners, estimated to be at least £157m. I, along with 50,000 other shareholders felt somewhat aggrieved, and subsequently contributed to the Railtrack Private Shareholders Action Group (RPSAG), whose objective was to prove that the Government minister responsible had cheated the shareholders of their investment.

During the subsequent court hearing interesting details emerged that indicated the machinations of an administration, which thought it could confiscate a company from its owners. One interesting revelation referred to a Government advisor who referred to the shareholders as 'grannies', who would not be liable to sue, as they would be satisfied with bus passes. On the last day of the trial, Stephen Byers, who had resigned in 2002, as the Government minister responsible at the time, said that he was not truthful to MPs about events leading to the collapse of Railtrack, and that he could not remember why he had not told the truth.

For those who cannot recall the result of RPSAG vs UK Government, the Judge concerned ruled in favour of the Government. The judgement disappointed and perplexed the main claimant, Mr Geoffrey Weir, who issued a statement on 14th October 2005, that included the following:

"Anybody who sat through the trial will find the Judge's conclusions bizarre. He seems to have attributed to a number of documents the least likely interpretation. In doing so he has reached a decision which we cannot accept as right. For instance, his definition of what constitutes a liar, as regards Mr Byers, is confused in the extreme. Apparently admitting lying to Parliament does not make you a proven liar. Nor does the Judge consider the Government teams' various references to our members as 'grannies' to be dismissive or derogatory. He considers it almost a

term of endearment. We will consider whether there are grounds to appeal."

Subsequently, I, along with others received a letter, dated 8th November 2005, from the chairman of RPSAG, which included the following:

'It is the advice of our lawyers that there is no realistic chance of winning an appeal. This is because the Judge's findings are interpretations of fact, rather than the interpretation of law.'

'We have taken on a powerful Government that has behaved disgracefully throughout this affair. We believe the evidence clearly shows that the Government engineered the administration of Railtrack behind the scenes for political purposes, sidelining the management and the regulator, in an attempt to avoid paying shareholders the proper value for their assets.'

Summarising, it would appear that ownership does matter, dependant upon who the owner is, and last, but not least, it is sometimes difficult to know who the owner is.

LIFE LONGEVITY
(Smoking, eating, sitting and light exercise?)

In the mid 1990s, statistics showed that the Japanese lived longer than any other nation. At the time the Japanese had an overall life expectancy of almost 83 years. I noticed as a non-smoker that most of the Japanese that I came into contact with, smoked. I also noticed whilst acting as host in the UK, that most Japanese, given the choice, preferred to eat in Chinese restaurants.

As a repeated host to one Japanese guest I raised the subject of their national longevity and asked, politely, what he thought the reasons for this were, and, even more politely, suggested that they would possibly live even longer if they did not smoke. My Japanese guest looked at me straight in the eye, paused, and said:

"Smoking has nothing to do with it, it is what you eat. You in the West eat rubbish."

When I was in Japan, after two weeks of eating Japanese food, I felt better than I had for years. The only instance I felt off-colour, was after dining at an expensive European restaurant where we had been taken for a special treat. I should add in all fairness that I was unaware at the time that I had gallstones.

What was noticeable in Japan were the large numbers of elderly people who were considerably sprightlier than their western counterparts. I do not recall seeing any joggers, but do recall seeing elderly people performing slow motion routines first thing in the morning.

Also noticeable was that in many restaurants the Japanese sat on the floor with their legs crossed, eating from low tables.

Western guests would also sit at low tables but with sunken floors underneath the tables, so that they would be able to sit in the western manner, as if on a backless chair.

Nowadays, I cannot help but notice the many veteran members of my golf club who have had knee and hip replacements to overcome arthritis. I nowadays, find it difficult to play with my grandson at floor level, in spite of taking daily doses of fish oil.

Apart from smoking, it would appear that the Japanese lifestyle of eating, sitting and slow motion exercise has a lot going for it.

GLOBALISATION
(Outsourcing by another name?)

In the late 1990s the company I was working for belonged to an Industry Trades Association. The Trades Association held occasional dinner meetings in London, where members would listen to and discuss matters concerning the industry.

During one such meeting, a colleague and myself were having an interesting conversation with the Managing Director of a company that supplied similar products to that of our company. During the conversation, we were interrupted. The person who interrupted us asked the Managing Director what his job was. The Managing Director turned around and said:

"I am a caretaker." Upon seeing the surprised reaction, the Managing Director then went on to explain that the process he was responsible for, normally originated in Germany, where the process produced a product for a unit cost of 20p. The process would then be moved to France where the product would be produced for a cost of 18p. After a further interval the process would be moved to the UK where the product would be produced for a cost of 15p. Subsequent moves would be to Spain and Poland, where the product would be produced for costs of 12p and 8p respectively.

Finally, the manufacturing process would move to China where the product would end up costing 3p.

Seeing that the interrupter was somewhat bemused, the Managing Director then said:

"During the time the manufacturing process is in the UK, I look after it. I am in fact, a caretaker."

With hindsight, it would probably have been more truthful if that Managing Director had said *temporary* caretaker.

However amusing this anecdote may, or may not be, it does pose some home truths, not least the obvious question as to who benefits from such transactions. Is it the company shareholders? Is it the company workforce? Is it the company management? Is it the company customers? Is it HM Revenue & Customs? A possible answer to these questions may best be understood from the following scenario.

Imagine that you are a Government employee, employed by the Ministry of Defence (MoD), and that you are responsible for a new £5 million four year contract for the supply of socks for the UK Army and that your remit is to obtain the best price for the socks which have to comply with MoD specifications. Imagine too that there are two suppliers, Supplier A and Supplier B. Supplier A is a 128 years old UK company that has supplied socks to the British Military for 80 years, and has its manufacturing facilities in the UK. Supplier B is a seven-year-old joint venture company that obtains its socks from manufacturing facilities in China but has a warehouse in the UK. Supplier B submits the cheaper price. To whom would you give the contract? The implications for choosing Supplier B will result in UK workers being made redundant, a reduction in HMRC tax receipts, an increasing overhead burden on Supplier A with the increasing possibility of bankruptcy and last, but not least, the British Army being reliant on its sock supply on a country from the opposite side of the world whose political views do not always agree with those held by the UK Government. The possible implications for choosing Supplier A are that you will not be helping any bonus system that has been incorporated into your pay for savings made and you will also miss the possibility of expense paid trips to

China to verify compliance with your procedures. To help assuage any misgivings in your decision a newly installed computer system can be blamed for any criticism made against you.

In the event that the above scenario may seem utterly ridiculous, the reader should substitute Supplier A with H J Hall Ltd of Leicester, Supplier B with Cooneen Watts and Stone of Tyrone, and the question asked in the House of Commons in July 2010, by the Bosworth MP Mr Tredinnick to Mr Peter Luff, minister responsible for defence equipment, concerning the loss of a £5million contract by H J Hall Ltd.

Finally, the reader may also wish to ponder over the £40 million bonuses paid to MoD personnel, headline news in the *Sunday Telegraph* February 19, 2012.

CENTRES OF EXCELLENCE
(Pontificating piffle?)

The expression 'Centres of Excellence' became fashionable in management circles during the 1990s. 'This is our Centre of Manufacturing Excellence', for example, has a certain resonance if delivered in an appropriate manner by someone of suitable stature. This is especially true if delivered in front of a receptive and compliant audience, such as on TV for example.

In the mid 1990s, I was attending the daily car build quality assessment meeting, at a German car plant. The cars produced the previous day were being assessed as normal, as they were at other car plants belonging to that organisation. In addition to the production cars, there were prototypes of a new model for which the company for whom I worked for, 'XYZ Ltd', had won the contract for the design and part manufacture of certain key components. The reason for my presence was to represent the company and note if our designs were acceptable to the car plant as opposed to their Design Office. In addition to the normal plant personnel being present, so too were our German competitors. The main assessor was the German Plant Manager, a towering dominating personality, with a powerful voice and a superb grasp of the English language. He looked at our parts that had been fitted to one of the prototypes. He picked up one of our parts that had been made with sponge rubber, passed some remarks in German, and then proceeded to walk slowly towards me with the product held aloft for all to see. He reached me, looked me in the eye, and with words everybody present could hear said slowly and loudly:

"XYZ Ltd – Centre of Manufacturing *Incompetence.*"

A meeting was held later that day to discuss our products in relation to the scheduled new car-launch. At the meeting I noticed the presence of an Asian on the German team, and, when the opportunity arose, glanced at his file, and realised he was the customers' Project Account Manager, and what was more, was British.

Two months later I was leaving my car at Heathrow Long Term Car Park, when I noticed the aforementioned Asian gentleman doing the same. I assumed he was going to the same destination in Germany. I approached him and introduced myself. He looked at me, paused, and apologised to say that he recognised me but did not know from where. I repeated my name and the name of my company. His eyes lit up, a smile crossed his face, and he said:

"Aaah – XYZ Ltd – Centre of Manufacturing *Incompetence.*"

We both proceeded to laugh in unison. We shared the same flight, I arranged to stop at his hotel, and thereafter we used to play pool together after we both completed our separate day's work at the car plant.

On the many occasions that I have since heard, and still hear the phrase 'This is our Centre of Excellence' I cannot help recall that particular meeting, that particular car plant, and visualising that particular German Manager, without a smile crossing my face, invariably coupled with the thought 'what a load of pontificating piffle'.

THE CUSTOMER COMES FIRST
(Do they really?)

One of the advantages of having the same company product manufactured in different countries is that it enables one to compare cultural differences, or to be more specific, the different national attitudes regarding work.

In the mid 1990s, my role with the grandiose title of Executive Programme Manager enabled me to be in such a position. The international company that I worked for had won a contract to supply parts to a major car company that produced the same model in three similar plants. The plants were situated in Germany, England and Spain. The car concerned had four variants. The first was a four-door Saloon, the second was a five door Estate, the third was a two door Coupé and the fourth variant was a specialised high performance model.

The plant in England built the four-door saloon only, and produced only for the UK market. The final section of the car assembly track, in all of the three car plants, involved each car being subjected to a car wash in an enclosure similar to that one sees at some petrol service stations. After the car wash, each car would be inspected for any sign of water ingress into the car via the doors, the boot and under the bonnet. Cars that failed the test were put on one side and the reasons for any leakages investigated. In the event that it was considered the fault of a supplier, the supplier would be summoned to the plant forthwith. The test is what one would expect from a car manufacturer. It gives a good indication of build quality as well as supplying the customer with a car that doesn't leak.

A question that you the reader, might ask is, "How would a plant cope in the event that too many cars leaked due to poor build quality?"

One way of tackling the issue, that also illustrates a disingenuous attitude to customers, became apparent when, during one of our visits to the British plant, we noticed that the cars were being stopped before the car wash. The car assembly workers then applied masking tape over the apertures of each car, after which the cars were then allowed to pass through the car wash. Following the car wash, the assembly workers removed the tape, after which the cars were then thoroughly inspected by white-coated inspectors.

What on earth, the reader might ask, was management doing to allow such nonsense? Upon reflection it should be apparent that everybody was happy with this arrangement. The assembly workers were being paid for doing additional work not in their job description, in addition, they were not criticised for their poor workmanship. The inspectors were working to their job description. The supervisors were not criticised by their managers, and senior management would be sat in their offices, reading reports indicating all was well on the car track with the build quality of the cars. The customers of course would not be happy nor would the car distributors when they would inevitably be inundated by customer complaints. However that scenario would not be apparent for a few weeks, or months later, and it would then be someone else's concern.

One lesson that this episode illustrates is the importance of seeing for oneself what is going on in the workplace as opposed to being told by subordinates, who will invariably tell you what you wish to hear.

The reader should bear the above in mind, when watching TV and hearing an organisation spokesperson (more often than not, a woman) apparently with all sincerity, saying the words: "In our organisation, the customer comes first."

SCIENTISTS AND ENGINEERS SHOULD BE ON TAP NOT ON TOP
(Do those on top know best?)

The above heading is regarded as having emanated from Sir Winston Churchill. It is often repeated in the UK by those in power who invariably have had a classical education and at heart regard science and particularly technology as anathemas. Irrespective of one's viewpoint, one would hope that those on top, irrespective of their education, are of the highest calibre and operate with the intention of serving the best interests of the country as a whole.

The rise of automobile usage during the twentieth century meant that the automobile offered increasing opportunities to increase revenue for the Government.

The initial annual Road Fund Licence was originally £6. In 1921, the 'horsepower tax' was introduced, replacing the Road Fund Licence. The annual tax was £1 per horsepower. The horsepower (HP) was based on a 1906 Royal Automobile Club (RAC) formula. It was derived by dividing the product of the number of cylinders (N) used in a car engine and the square of the engine cylinders diameter (D) in inches, by 2.5. Expressed mathematically the formula was: $HP = D^2N/2.5$.

The result was that the tax penalised cars having engines with large bores and a large number of cylinders, such as American imports. The immediate effect was that the Road Fund Licence of £6 was, for example, replaced with a tax of £23 for an American Ford Model T, and £12 for a British Morris Cowley. In the UK, the tax helped promote the design and use of engines having small diameter bores and long strokes. Car engines in the UK pre-1947 were invariably long stroke and small bore. An understanding of heat engines, in particular the Otto cycle, shows that the thermal efficiency of a petrol engine is dependant only on the compression ratio. In practice, for a given engine, a short stroke and a large bore combination produces both greater power and better fuel consumption than an equivalent engine having a long stroke and a small bore combination.

In short the use of the RAC formula for calculating horsepower was technical nonsense. The abolition of the tax in 1947 meant that engine designers were no longer restricted in the choice of stroke and bore ratio. In the event that an 'on tap' engineer, familiar with the theory and design of heat engines, had been 'tapped', engine development in the UK car industry would probably not have remained stagnant for 26 years.

In 2009 a Parliamentary Committee investigating engineering rejected the Government view that ministers had ample access to engineering advice. One story that seemed to sum up the MPs' scepticism was that concerning the development of the policy and the selection of sites for the Government's new eco-towns in the UK.

One of the proposed new 'carbon-neutral' solar and wind-powered new towns was on a site that was not feasible from infrastructure service considerations. The policy was, apparently, developed without engineering input, because the department entrusted with it was new, and no one thought there was a problem[1].

Basically it would appear that even on technical matters, being on tap doesn't mean you will be tapped, because those on top do not see the need. They in effect know best.

In 1990 only 0.9% of British MPs were engineers compared with 6.0% in the German Bundestag and 5.2% in the French

National Assembly. Not a single Civil Servant in the top two grades was a Chartered Engineer, whilst out of nearly 700 Civil Servants in the top four grades only 23 were Chartered Engineers. It might also be added that engineers do not do much better in regard to the UK's industrial and commercial elite[2].

Instead of promoting positive discrimination of sex, race or colour in the vetting of Ministers, MPs, Civil Servants and Company Directors, it would perhaps be better if such a policy promoted certain professions who are clearly left out in the cold.

Such a policy might not be an obvious vote winner, but it could be seen as an attempt to broaden a system that is repeatedly shown to be deficient and wanting. Such a system would however, discriminate against professional politicians.

The least one could expect is the recognition that a better mix of know-how at the top would serve the country better, irrespective of class, sex, race, religion or colour.

The saying 'Scientists and Engineers should be on tap and not on top' has gone beyond the realms of the UK Government and the UK Civil Service. It is a view clearly held by those at the top of UK industry. The results can be seen, to the detriment of the UK, whenever UK industry is contrasted with its equivalent in Germany and others.

Imagine if Sir Winston Churchill had said:

"Those educated in the Classics should be on tap and not on top."

In reality, Sir Winston was one such person so he would never have said it. However, in our complex technological society it does pose the obvious question:

'Are those educated in the Classics fit to be on top?' Even more to the point:

'In the event that those educated in the Classics were on tap and not on top, would *they* ever be tapped?'

References:

[1] Editorial comment. *Professional Engineering.* 8 April 2009. IMechE.

[2] Figures taken from an article by the historian Corelli Barnett in *Engineering First,* Issue no 3, The Journal of the Engineering Council. February 1997.

C9

OUTSOURCING
(Good management?)

Outsourcing is a fact of life in the UK today. Most people become aware of it whenever they phone up major service industries such as banks, gas or electricity. The term 'outsourcing' sounds much more modern than that of subcontracting or contracting out, which is what it basically is.

In any manufacturing organisation if orders have to be met in a given time, and those orders exceed the organisation's capacity to meet them, subcontractors are a standard solution.

In the early 1960s, my first job as Production Controller for large steam turbine diaphragms involved me using subcontractors. Subcontractors were an extra resource available in times of need.

In the late 1960s, I was the Development and Project Engineer of a company that manufactured a product that had many competitors. The Sales (marketing) Department preferred to place orders with the company's competitors. It was easier, and caused less hassle. The Sales Department negotiated, arranged a price and added on 10%. They didn't have to listen to excuses from their own manufacturing department who were invariably struggling to meet demand. The Sales Department actually believed that they didn't need the manufacturing department at all, especially as it got in their way of doing business from a position of strength.

In the rubber industry, mouldings made from rubber invariably require trimming. The excess rubber or flash from rubber moulded products can be removed cryogenically, cold trimmed manually, on or off the premises, hot trimmed directly, as the product comes hot off the press, or a combination of any of the aforementioned. Trimming is a major problem in the rubber moulding industry and is one of the reasons why the use of thermoplastic elastomers is increasing. The subcontracting or outsourcing of hand trimming operations has considerable advantages, not the least of which is cost. The result is that the trimming of rubber mouldings can form what are basically cottage industries within the vicinity of the factories producing rubber products. There will be those who regard this activity as exploitation. The trimmers are not being paid the 'going rate' would be one such argument. There will be those who will recognise the advantages from the trimmers' viewpoint, namely an operation that can be done at home at any time of their choosing. For those capable of doing two or more things at once, such as chatting, child-minding and watching TV, earning money trimming, has attractions. Other advantages of off site trimming for the industry are that it avoids issues such as sex discrimination, contracts of employment, absenteeism, payment equality issues and high labour costs for a basically simple but essential operation. The big disadvantage is that it requires considerable control, covering issues such as product quality, delivery, collection and payment. All these were issues, amongst others, that I was responsible for as the Manufacturing Director of rubber product manufacturing companies in the 1980s and 1990s.

If we consider all of the above, it does not require too much imagination to realise that if everything is subcontracted or outsourced, then further advantages may ensue, there would be no on site labour problems, no need to invest in capital plant, there would be no bureaucratic interference, there would be lower costs, greater profits and the opportunity to pay oneself salary rises and bonuses. The type of organisation that could exploit this situation would invariably be a monopoly supplier. One such example is household waste disposal, which is the responsibility of local authorities. Many local authorities subcontract the whole operation to private companies. The customer pays rates to the local authorities for the service and has no other choice.

Large organisations are in a position to exploit the principle of outsourcing even further by in effect obtaining loans from the subcontractors themselves as a condition of the subcontractors doing business with them. This scenario may strike the reader as both unlikely and unethical. Supermarkets and other large retailers for example, are often criticised for not paying their suppliers until their supplied goods are sold. In effect, the suppliers to the supermarkets are financing their customer, the supermarket itself. The suppliers to the supermarkets often have no other choice. In this particular instance, the ultimate customer, you, the reader has.

Private Finance Initiatives (PFIs) operated by local authorities and the Government is another example. In this case the contractor finances a project and then gets paid by the local authority or Government over an agreed period of time after the project has been completed. The flaw in this latter case is that debt is created. The debt has to be paid off sometime in the future. For local authorities and the Government this is no problem, as they are in a position to increase rates and taxes annually. Unlike the situation with supermarkets, the ultimate customer, you, the reader, has no choice in the matter.

Is outsourcing good management? It would appear that the answer depends upon whether the organisation is run for the benefit of the managers themselves or for their customers.

C10

PROFIT
(Economics or Ideology?)

Anybody working in private industry is fully aware of the
importance of profit for the wellbeing of the Company. Profit is
the amount that remains after wages, salaries, company running
costs, debts, dividends and taxes have been deducted from the
revenue taken from the sales of the Company's products. A
private company that habitually does not make a profit becomes
bankrupt.

In simple terms in order to make a profit the price of a
product must exceed the cost of producing that product. This
can be expressed with formula (A):

[Price = Cost + Profit]

In words this formula says that Price is the result of adding
profit to cost.

In mathematical terms this simple formula can also be
expressed with formula (B):

[Profit = Price − Cost]

In words this formula says that Profit is the result of
subtracting cost from the price.

The formula can also be expressed as formula (C):

[Price − Cost = Profit]

In words this formula says that for a given Price, Profit is
the result of having subcontracted Cost from that Price. Whilst
these nuances may seem trivial, their importance becomes
apparent if we consider the situation from the viewpoint of a

customer who not only has a choice of supplier, but also has the choice of what they are prepared to pay for the item in question.

Let us assume that a customer is prepared to pay £500 for a given item and that you wish to make a profit of £100. If the item cost £400 then using formula (C), [Price -Cost = Profit] a profit of £100 will have been made.

Using formula (B), [Profit = Price - Cost] a profit of £100 would also be made if the cost is £400. A profit of £100 could also be made in the event that you could persuade the customer to pay £600 as a result of you adding embellishments resulting in a product cost of £500.

The significance of formula (A) [price = cost + profit] is completely different from the other two formulae.

Let us assume that your cost is £500. You will clearly not get a profit of £100 unless the price was £600. You may well argue that the cost of £500 is a good and fair price. The customer on the other hand would argue that only a fool would pay £600 for an item that could be obtained for £500 elsewhere. In the event that you sold the item for what the customer was prepared to pay (£500) you will have made no profit and would be well on the way to bankruptcy.

It can clearly be seen that formula (C), [Price – Cost = Profit], is the only formula of the three that emphasises lowering costs. In the event that you could lower your cost to £300 a profit of £200 would be made. This eventuality would of course lead to certain political types frothing at the mouth in their denunciation of their perception of excess profit and exploitation. (See chapter titled OWNERSHIP-Ferranti Bloodhound missile).

The perception of profit is in many circles regarded as exploitation. This viewpoint becomes especially apparent when the NHS, the largest employer in Europe is discussed. It is perceived that the use of any alternative organisation that makes a profit whilst providing care to patients must be resisted at all costs. There appears to be little rational discussion on the matter. In this viewpoint the meaning of the word profit would appear to have moved from the realm of economics to that of ideology. Can this dichotomy be resolved? A simple case study involving myself will perhaps throw some light on this very issue.

In the late 1970's I was the 'works manager' of a small company. One Saturday morning whilst commissioning a machine I trapped my left hand as a result of which I lost $2^1/_2$ fingers. As this was an industrial injury I automatically became entitled to compensation under the National Insurance Scheme and eventually attended an appointment for injury assessment. The assessment appointment consisted of the following sequence:

1. Receiving a letter informing me of the date and time for assessment.

2. Reporting to a receptionist, at the appointed time. The receptionist took my details and instructed me to sit down alongside other applicants, and wait for my name to be called.

3. My name was called and I was escorted by a nurse to a cubicle and asked to provide a urine sample into a container provided for me. My protestations that this was both irrelevant and unnecessary were brushed aside. I was then asked to return to my seat and await a further recall.

4. My name was again called, whereupon I was escorted by another nurse to a cubicle that contained a desk behind which sat two doctors.

5. I was asked to sit down and place my hand on the desk.

6. One of the doctors made a hand sketch of my injury and the two doctors discussed my injury between themselves, commenting on such matters as the effectiveness of the skin graft.

When the two doctors had completed their business one of the doctors asked me what I thought. I answered, " I think it will be a long time before my fingers will grow again." The two doctors looked at each other in horror and one of them leaned over the desk and said to me very slowly, " Mr. Evans, your fingers are **not** going to grow again."

7. I left the premises somewhat relieved that I had not been taken to the local lunatic asylum escorted by two or more men in white coats.

It is obvious that cost had not been a consideration in devising the above procedure for injury assessment.

After obtaining professional advice concerning the possibility of obtaining compensation for my injury I decided to sue my employer notwithstanding the possible repercussions. The subsequent assessment appointment consisted of the following sequence:

1. Receiving a letter informing me of the date and time for assessment.

2. Reporting to a receptionist at the appointed time. The receptionist took my details and directed me to an office in which was a desk behind which sat a doctor.

3. The doctor asked me to sit down, looked at my hand and then asked various questions, which included, "Are you left handed or right handed?" "What is your occupation and what do you do?" The doctor then asked me to perform certain tasks such as tying my shoelaces, gripping his hand, first with my right hand and then with my left hand.

4. I left the premises in a happy frame of mind.

This latter procedure for injury assessment was clearly more cost effective than the former. Not only was the procedure more cost effective it was also more customer orientated. The second procedure was that of a private practice, the first procedure was that of the state NHS. It does not take too much imagination to realise that a private practice operating the NHS injury assessment procedure would soon be bankrupt, not only because of cost issues but also because anybody with a choice would not go willingly to a practice operating such procedures.

The basic difference between the two procedures is that cost is a consideration in one and not in the other.

In the event that such and similar issues concerning the NHS are discussed on the BBC the topic invariably orientates towards profit issues and not those of cost. The NHS system is regarded as pure as it is not contaminated with the profit motive. In essence formula (A), [Price = Cost + Profit] is used, with Profit being zero. The situation would be different if formula (C), [Price – Cost = Profit] was used, as the emphasis would then be on reducing costs.

On the basis of my personal case study, it would appear that NHS procedures could ultimately bankrupt the nation.

The UK political obsession with profit, and not cost, is not only restricted to the NHS and the BBC.

The Supermarine Spitfire was an aeroplane that is embedded in the national psyche. The Spitfire was a key participant in the WWII battle of Britain and was active throughout the war in its various modifications. The same was also true of the German equivalent, the Messerschmitt ME 109. The build time for a Spitfire Mark VC airframe amounted to 13,000 man-hours. The build time for the Messerschmitt ME 109G airframe amounted to 4,000 man-hours [1]. The UK government concerns were those of profit control and not cost reduction. In the event that there had been no war, and the two aeroplanes were competing in an open market, which of the two would have been the more successful?

In many ways the application of formula (A), [Price = Cost + Profit] can be regarded as a root cause of many of the problems that beset UK manufacturing and service industries.

In the event that the customer does not agree to the price, somebody, more often than not the Government, has to step in and impose the price attempting at the same time to ensure that the profit does not exceed what is considered fair. An issue demonstrating this approach is provided by the current political stances regarding the energy industry.

Accountants think in terms of formula (A): [Price = Cost + Profit]

An Industrial Engineer concentrates on lowering costs. Costs and their associated components are items to be analysed and lowered rather than calculated.

Industrial Engineers think in terms of formula (C): [Price – Cost = Profit]

UK industry favours accountants. Japanese and German industry favours Industrial Engineers.

It would appear that the UK Government also favours accountants, with the emphasis being on restricting profits as shown in chapters titled OWNERSHIP and ACCOUNTANTS.

References:

1. Ministry of Aircraft Production (AVIA Series) AVIA 10/269 Labour statistics.

Further suggested reading on this subject matter:

The Audit of War, author Correlli Barnett, publisher faber and faber.

Workplace Management, author Taiichi Ohno, publisher Productivity Press.

Section D

HISTORICAL PERSPECTIVES

'The only thing men learn from history is that men learn nothing from history.'

Georg Wilhelm Friedrich Hegel
1770-1831

LESSONS WILL BE LEARNED
(Can pigs fly?)

Whenever a spokesman or spokeswoman appears on TV to explain a disaster within their organisation, the explanation always seems to end with the words:

"We are looking at our procedures and lessons will be learned."

As a youngster I recall my father telling me that as a seven-year-old, he, along with his brothers and sisters, spent the night cowering underneath their beds whilst Zeppelin L21 was dropping bombs that landed in streets near to where they lived in Bolton. Prior to this 1916 domestic event, in 1908, the Admiralty concerned with Count Zeppelin's activities in Germany, ordered a rigid airship from Vickers Ltd. The airship ordered was larger than the contemporary Zeppelins and in addition was to be the first airship to be constructed using duralumin, an aluminium alloy. His Majesty's Airship No.1, subsequently called 'Mayfly', possessed a ship's anchor, Honduras mahogany woodwork and a rigid keel.[1]When completed, it was found to be far too heavy to fly. In order to lighten the airship a major decision was taken to remove the keel. The modified airship was too weak and subsequently broke in two when being towed out of its hangar in 1911. It was damaged beyond repair and never flew.

Arguments ensued between HM Government and Vickers Ltd concerning the ownership of the wreck. The First Lord of the Admiralty prevented the minutes and findings of the disaster from publication. However, as was said at the time: "Lessons will be learned."

Towards the end of the First World War the Government placed an order with Short Bros to produce an airship for Atlantic patrols. The result was the R38.

At the end of the war the unfinished R38 was offered to the Americans. The Americans had been thwarted in their attempts to buy direct from the German Zeppelin Company. In 1921, the R38, painted in USA markings had her final test flight over the North Sea. After a day and a night the tests were radioed to have been successfully completed. As the airship cruised low over Hull an order was given to execute a series of violent turns, as a result of which the airship broke into two parts. An explosion and a fire followed, with the result that the airship ended up in the Humber Estuary. Of the 49 crew aboard, 44 were killed. Following the R38 disaster it was revealed by the Aeronautical Research Committee that the Civil Servants concerned omitted aerodynamic force calculations in their design calculations[1]. Lessons were no doubt learned.

In 1923 Vickers Ltd put forward a proposal to the Government to build six commercial airships. Following a General Election the Government changed, and the first Labour Government came into power. There was a nucleus of Civil Servants in the Air Ministry associated with the R38 who considered that they were in a better position to build airships than were Vickers Ltd[2]. A Government Cabinet committee was subsequently set up and decided that:

'The Air Ministry at Cardington shall build an airship of a certain size, load–carrying capacity and speed, and Vickers Ltd shall build another to the same specification. By this ingenious device we shall find out which is the better principle, capitalism or state enterprise.'

The airship representing state enterprise was the Air Ministry airship R101. The airship representing capitalism was the Vickers airship R100.

In the five years that elapsed before either ship flew, neither the designer of the R101, Lieutenant-Colonel V C Richmond, nor the designer of the R100, Mr B N Wallis, visited each other's works, nor did they meet or correspond with each other.

When the ships were ready, the Vickers airship R100 had a tare weight of 102 tons and a gross lift of 156 tons, giving it 54 tons useful lifting weight. The maximum speed was 81 mph. The Air Ministry airship R101 had a tare weight of 113 tons and a gross lift of 148 tons giving it 35 tons useful lifting weight. The R101's useful lifting weight of 35 tons was considered insufficient, and an additional gas bay was added which resulted in a final useful lifting weight of 49 tons. The maximum speed was reported to be 70 mph. The reasons for the large discrepancy between the two airships built to the same specification were many. The Air Ministry R101 Airship was powered by five diesel engines and its structure consisted of 16 vertical polygonal frames with each frame having 15 sides. Steel and duralumin were used in equal measure[3]. The Vickers R100 Airship was powered by four petrol engines, and its entire duralumin structure contained only 11 different parts and 15 different joints.

The Engineer magazine at the time thought that the Air Ministry R101 Airship was a triumph of engineering design[4]. (The reader may wonder what the description of the Vickers R100 Airship would have been in comparison.)

On July 29, 1930, after completing over 150 hrs and 5,000 miles of trial flights, the Vickers airship R100 departed on its maiden flight to Canada where it received a tremendous welcome upon its arrival. Over 100,000 people visited the airship daily, during its twelve-day sojourn in Montreal. The Vickers R100 also made 24-hour passenger carrying flights to Ottawa, Toronto and

Niagara Falls. Following a 57½ hour return flight, the Vickers R100 docked back in the UK, on August 16 1930, unsung, and never flew again.

On October 4, 1930, following 16 hours of trials done three days earlier, Air Ministry airship R101, without a certificate of airworthiness, took off on its maiden flight to India. It crashed into a French hillside at Allone, near Beauvais, France. Of the 54 persons on board only six survived. Those killed included the chief designer, Colonel Richmond, and Baron Thomson of Cardington, Secretary of State for Air, rumoured at the time to become the next Viceroy of India, and the driving personality behind the R101 from its conception.

The court of enquiry under Sir John Simon found that the cause of the crash had been caused by a leakage of gas from one or more bags in the fore part of the airship. The glowing reports given by the Air Ministry and Government concerning the airworthiness and competence of the airship were in direct contradiction of the technical and support staff who worked on the R101, and also the observations of those working on the R100.

The whole episode, intended to show the superiority of state enterprise over capitalism did not end up the way envisaged by the Government, despite the resources expended on the State Enterprise Air Ministry R101.

The Zeppelin Company bought five tons of duralumin from the site of the R101 wreckage. The Government ordered that the Vickers R100 be broken up and sold for scrap. The Vickers R100 was crushed with a steamroller and sold to a London metal merchant for less than £600. It was suspected by some at the time that the latter action was one of pure vindictiveness. With no further orders from the Government the Vickers R100 staff were disbanded.

The aeronautical engineer Nevil Shute Norway, better known as the novelist Nevil Shute, succeeded Barnes Wallis to become the chief engineer of the Vickers R100 project. In his autobiography *Slide Rule,* first published in 1953, Nevil Shute gives a detailed account of the development of both the R100 and R101 airships. His account of the R101 disaster is not only critical of the R101 design and management team, but also damning in his condemnation of the senior civil servants and politicians involved, especially concerning the issue of the certificate of airworthiness.

The reader should reflect upon the above whenever they see or hear a spokesperson, particularly from a Government organisation, saying:

'We are looking at our procedures and lessons will be learned.'

References:

[1] *Airshipwreck.* Len Deighton & Arnold Schwartzman. Book Club Associates

[2] *Slide Rule.* Nevil Shute. Autobiography. Vintage Books. ISBN 9780099530176

[3] Boulton and Paul – the R101. Extract from *Boulton and Paul Aircraft-since 1915*

[4] *The Innovative Engineer.* Published by Morgan-Grampian Ltd 1981. The Airship.

D2

HEALTH AND SAFETY
(Service industry par excellence?)

In 1966, a massive spoil heap collapsed into the Welsh village of Aberfan, burying 20 homes and a primary school. One hundred and sixteen children and 28 adults died in the disaster. The subsequent Davies Tribunal Report on the disaster was highly critical of the National Coal Board (NCB) and its chairman, Alfred Robens.

In the wake of the disaster Robens refused to allow the NCB to fund the removal of the remaining coal tips around Aberfan. The coal tips' removal were eventually funded by money taken from the public disaster relief fund. In 1969 Robens, whilst still Chairman of the NCB, was selected by Barbara Castle to chair a committee on workplace health and safety. The result was the Robens Report, published in 1972. The Report itself led to the Health & Safety at Work act 1974, the creation of the Health & Safety Commission and the Health & Safety Executive (HSE).

In 1974, I, along with other members of staff, attended a meeting held in the Works Managers office to discuss the implications of the Health & Safety at Work Act. I recall making an observation of the date, which was April 1, and receiving an appropriate reprimand.

Other than HM Armed Services, one would have thought that with the various Factories Acts that there was already sufficient legislation in place to deter killing, maiming and the forcing of staff to work in situations hazardous to their health.

It may even cross the mind of any rational person to consider what benefits are there to an employer to treat their staff in anything other than a sensible manner. It would appear that there must be many irrational uncaring employers. It would be very illuminating to commission a study to find out what percentage of managers are potential psychopaths or megalomaniacs. The Government clearly assumes that they exist in private industry. What about the Civil Service and Government? In private industry you can at least change your job once you recognise the type.

In a legislative act, the interpretation and the meaning of the words used, is decided by the legal profession. What really matters to any business or individual is how the interpretations of a legislative act compare with the intentions envisaged. The Health and Safety at Work Act is a case in point. When the act was passed did those passing it envisage the following:

A five-step process involving phoning a contractor's hotline and the filling of a worksheet in order to change a light bulb, as was apparently the case at Kent police's two new privately owned super-stations.

Insurers, in the world plank walking championship, demanding that contestants be issued with warnings that they could get wet. Swale council's safety concerns nearly cancelled the event. The event was reprieved in the last minute with the provision of a 'water quality certificate'.

Chichester council allegedly refusing to clear a dustbin from a stream, four inches deep, because none of the staff were qualified to wear the necessary safety equipment to stop the staff from being swept away.

The situation is now so out of control that the HSE (Health and Safety Executive) publishes monthly myths on its website.

One would hope and expect that the implementation of Health and Safety concerns would concentrate on those areas that cause the most avoidable deaths, accidents and suffering.

In 2007 the Office for National Statistics figures showed that the total number of deaths attributed to the super-bugs MRSA and Clostridium-Difficile, were 5,981.

The Department of Transport figures for 2007 showed that the number of deaths in road accidents were 2,946.

The HSE figures for 2008 showed that a total of 229 workers lost their lives at work in the UK.

In June 2009, following a three-month HSE consultation with bosses, industry representatives, trade unions, members of parliament and employees, the HSE announced a ten-point strategy to tackle death and injury at work.

Summarising: In a 12 month period when 5,981 deaths were caused by super-bugs, 2,946 deaths on our roads and 229 deaths in our factories, the HSE, after a three month consultation issued a ten-point plan to make people aware of their responsibilities in reducing the figure of 229 killed in the workplace. Harold Shipman alone is reported to have killed more than 229 of his patients. Is the NHS not a place of work? Is it not beyond the wit of our politicians to suggest that the HSE might be of use in sorting out the NHS super-bug and other related problems? It would appear that the NHS is politically untouchable. It is run by the Civil Service, as is the HSE. The largest employer in Europe is not even considered for inclusion in the HSE statistics for deaths.

Health & Safety pervades the working environment of every company in the UK. It affects all citizens. The interpretations of the Health and Safety Act are clearly not what were intended.

Industry in the UK is now a shadow of what it was in 1974 when the act was first published. The Act was intended to protect the workforce both from itself and management. It now appears to be used to protect management from being sued by a populace encouraged to do so by members of the legal profession. The Act has created an industry of its own, and it would appear that the Civil Service, legislators, the legal profession and unions, relish and thrive on it.

It could be argued that Health and Safety has now become an essential and established part of the UK Service Industry.

TRADE UNIONS
(Biting the hand that feeds you?)

Trade Unions have made a big impact on the work environment in the UK. Their presence could not be ignored throughout my working life.

After graduating in 1964, my first real job was production controller for large steam turbine diaphragms in a large electrical manufacturing company.

The various manufacturing stages in the production of diaphragms included casting, forging, fabrication, machining operations, assembly, and inspection. There were a multitude of unions on site that covered all trades. The Amalgamated Engineering Union (AEU) was the dominant union for the skilled operatives, namely those involved in machining operations. The majority of unskilled operatives were represented by the General Municipal Workers Union (GMWU). The union view at the time was that if you did more than your allotted job you were depriving someone else of their job. A good example of this in practice was when I was confronted with an impasse whereby no diaphragms were progressing beyond a particular bespoke machine that basically cut support slots into the side of the diaphragm perimeters. The machine operator was absent through illness. Neither the Foreman nor other operators capable of operating the machine would do so. My solution was to obtain a drawing modification that enabled the slots to be cut in a different shape by other machines. This in effect made the bespoke machine and operator redundant, however normal operations resumed once the operator returned to work.

Over-manning was rampant and was accepted practice throughout the workplace.

A good example was the manning of single cutter planing machines. These huge machines once set up would sometimes run for days without the need of any operator involvement. One man could have operated all the planing machines with occasional help. In practice two men operated each planing machine, one the operator, the other the helper. Their working days were spent moving to and fro as they stood on one end of the moving bed of the planing machine. (Readers may see such a machine on the web: 'Butler planing machine – You Tube').

Why, the reader may ask, did management allow the above and other such similar practices to flourish in supposedly competitive industries?

In the late nineteenth century an American engineer, Frederick Winslow Taylor, challenged the inefficiencies in industrial working practices. Following his involvement in developing High Speed Steel (HSS), which changed both cutting tool manufacture and machine tool design, Taylor turned his attention to the men who worked the machine tools and studied the work they were doing. After three years at Bethlehem Steel Taylor was fired as a result of the opposition of other managers. The ideas that he had tried to implement at Bethlehem Steel were published in 1911 in a book titled, *The principles of scientific management*. The publication of the book raised a storm in USA and in the UK. The terms 'motion study' and 'Taylorism' were added to the English vocabulary. An example of the feelings engendered by the book were the views of the editor of the journal *The Engineer* May19,1911, concerning the use of route cards:

For heavens sake let us leave the freeman who works for us something on which to exercise his intelligence, something to make him higher than the machines he operates, and to give him a right still to call himself a man.

The journal's alternative to Taylor's ideas was the incentive of a premium bonus associated with rate-fixing, not those associated with stop watch time study. This was seen as encouraging worker initiative as well as giving a chance of earning more. (See chapter titled INCENTIVES). *The Engineer* envisaged the potential of human ingenuity overcoming the potential inefficiency of such a system.

On April 12, 1912, under the heading 'Taylorism again' *The Engineer* commented on a US Government inquiry concerning proposals to adopt Taylor's ideas in the US State factories. The article went on to quote the British Consul General in New York:

'Between the ages of forty and fifty, when the European workman is at his best, the American frequently breaks down, physical exhaustion, dyspepsia, or nervous prostration follows, and the man's life as a worker is done.'

There were however some doubts expressed in the same article concerning the way events were unfolding, it suggested that *'extreme systemisation was liable to breed feelings in the men which go to feed socialistic tendencies and to crush out of them the desire to excel which all right-minded artisans should have.'* The editor went on:

'Unfortunately, the men's own trade unions exert a strong influence in the same direction, for they avowedly have the intention to reduce individualism to a minimum and to discount all development of technical skill by restricting output and bringing the day's work for all to a monotonous dead level[1].' The latter perceptive comment, concerning Trade Unions, made 100 years ago in a technical journal, indicated a root cause of poor UK

productivity that a myriad of subsequent Government publications and policies never effectively tackled. The UK working environment, both within and without British industry, lived with the consequences throughout my career and is still living with them today.

In the early 1960s my second job was that of a Development Engineer in a chemical works that amongst other chemicals produced a blue dye for use in jeans. The blue dye was supplied in liquid, pellet and powder form. The production process used chemicals that were extremely corrosive. The bespoke plant had been designed by chemists and engineers who had little or no understanding of the material properties of the equipment and components used in the production process, with the result that chemicals leaked throughout the process, and were present throughout the plant. One could walk through the plant wearing a safety helmet, protective smock, gloves, scarf and safety glasses, touch nothing, and come out visually blue. The main union at the plant was the Chemical Workers Union (CWU). Other unions included the General Municipal Workers Union (GMWU), the Amalgamated Engineering Union (AEU), and the Electrical Trades Union (ETU). An example of the thought process of the CWU shop steward is perhaps best illustrated with the following example:

The management had decided to place safety helmets at the entrance of a concrete building where signs of flaking had been noticed. Anybody entering the building could help themselves to one of the safety helmets conveniently available in racks.

The CWU Shop Steward banned his members from wearing the helmets unless they were paid danger money. The safety helmets were subsequently withdrawn. Another safety initiative that had been adopted by the company management was a statistical approach that involved recording hazards encountered whilst walking a given route in a given time. This entailed the use of a hazard matrix chart mounted on a clipboard, complete with a stopwatch. A comparison of the charts over a period of time, gave an indication whether safety precautions and good housekeeping practices were improving or deteriorating. The use of stopwatches was an anathema to the AEU, one of whose Shop Stewards would accompany the checker to ensure he was not secretly timing any of his members, even though the activities of his members were mainly of a maintenance nature.

The effect of these and similar obstructive practices on management thinking regarding unions is perhaps illustrated at my third job where in the mid 1960s I was the plant Mechanical Engineer, responsible for contractors and modification work in a continuous process plant. Head Office had requested that a detailed report be compiled of all site contractors. The details requested included, the contractors business, number of employees, turnover, profitability, unions and anything else that may have been considered of relevance. The task for completing this request was handed to me.

It was relatively easy to list the contractors that the company used. Obtaining the details was a different matter and required making phone calls, which was no problem with those contractors with whom I was familiar. For other contractors, the response in too many instances was a variation of, "Who do you think you are?" with the result that I decided that the best course of action would be to guess or fabricate the details required. The resultant report consisted of a mixture of facts and fiction. My conscience was clear in that no harm was done. Head Office got its report and I could proceed doing what I considered my job.

Sometime after the report had been submitted the plant Electrical Engineer came to me and said something along the lines, "Guess what Head Office have done, they have banned me from using Company X, it is a disaster and will result in the plant shutdown."

"Why have they done that?" I asked.

"Because they have received a report informing them that company X have employees belonging to the Association of Scientific Technical and Managerial Staffs (ASTMS), and they will not deal with any company involved with that union," he replied. The remedy was relatively simple, I modified that section of the report, and another lesson was learned for the future.

In the late 1960s I was working for an American company as a Project Engineer, whose antipathy towards unions was very noticeable, particularly in the USA, where sites evaluated for plant relocations had to be in union free areas. When assessing sites in the UK, if I had proposed areas that were known for bad industrial relationships, I would have expected to be given short shrift or worse.

It should be noted that at a much later date, the Japanese with a much more thorough approach to employing personnel, did succeed in such areas.

Unions were heavily involved in the creation of the 1964 Industrial Training Act. The Act in effect replaced all Company Apprenticeship Schemes with regional Industrial Training Boards (ITBs), funded by levies paid by all companies within the industries concerned. At the time it was considered that five-year craft apprenticeships, (future trade union members) were too long, they were considered a source of cheap labour for employers and often resulted in poaching from other employers who did not organise apprenticeship schemes. Industrial Tribunals emanated from the 1964 Industrial Training Act. The name Industrial Tribunal was changed to Employment Tribunal under the Employment Rights (Dispute Resolution) Act 1998.

As a result of dismissing an employee I had first hand experience of an Industrial Tribunal in the early 1980s. The records made at the trial by the tribunal were hand written. It was a very interesting experience and took virtually all day. Whilst the company won the case it was apparent that one had to have very clear written records and procedures in place to satisfy the Judge.

Today, it is difficult to convey the innumerable ways in which the activities of shop stewards disrupted and dominated management time during the 1960s and 1970s. Most strikes were unofficial.

The Royal Commission on Trade Unions and Employers' Associations 1965-1968, known as the Donovan Report, was published in 1968[2]. The Report contained interesting facts, for example:

In 1967 of the 26 million people in work 23.75 million (15 million male, 8.75 female) were employees. There were 9 million in manufacturing, 3.5 million in industries such as gas, electricity and coalmining, 3.25 million in financial, professional and scientific services, 1.5 million in national and local Government services and 3.5 million in transport, communication, building and construction.

The Report showed that 95% of industrial stoppages were due to unofficial strikes.

The four industries that consistently had the poorest strike records were, coalmining, the docks, shipbuilding and motor manufacturing. The principle causes of such strikes were reported to be wages, working arrangements and work terminations. The Report considered the use of law as being impractical in industrial relations. The practicalities of using the law were illustrated in Appendix 6, which detailed the case of 4,000 miners at the Betteshanger Colliery in Kent, who went on strike during the War in December 1941. Under the National Arbitration Order the strike was illegal, and, although the strike had the backing of the local Union Officials, the Secretary for Mines, with Cabinet backing, decided on prosecution. The prosecution decided to concentrate on 1,000 underground workers. Extra supplies of forms were rushed to the Chief

Constable of Kent. Several Justices of the Peace had to be found to sign 1,000 forms in duplicate and extra police were drafted in to serve them. On the basis that the proceedings would take months if everyone pleaded not guilty, the Union agreed that they would instruct their members to plead guilty, and accept the decision on a few test cases. Everybody pleaded guilty as agreed. The Branch Secretary was sentenced to two months with hard labour, the local President and an executive member one month each with hard labour. Thirty-five men were fined £3, or one month's imprisonment, and nearly 1,000 men were fined £1 or 14 days' imprisonment. There were protests against the severity of the sentences, but the key issue was that the only men who could call off the strike were now in jail. Negotiations were re-opened and apart from some face-saving words the three officials were released after spending eleven days in prison.

The mine reopened and in the first week the normal output of coal was nearly trebled. (Which makes one wonder what constituted a normal week.) The Clerk of Justices reported that of the 1,000 men who had been fined only nine had paid. As the county jail could only accommodate a few at a time he asked for guidance. The company asked if they could pay the fines on behalf of the men, as they wanted to avoid further trouble. They were told on no account to do this, and the court was advised not to enforce the unpaid fines. In 1950, eight years later and five years after the war had ended, the National Union of Mineworkers (NUM) formally asked that the £1 fine paid by the nine members be returned.

The Donovan report makes very interesting reading, throwing light on what is now a bygone age for manufacturing industry within the UK. The report had difficulty in defining a Trade Union and it could be argued that it skirted around the issues of restrictive practices and Trade Union political involvement. It certainly did not face the issue raised by the editor of *The Engineer* over 100 years earlier, *'Trade Unions avowedly have the intention to reduce individualism to a minimum and to discount all development of technical skill by restricting output and bringing the day's work for all to a monotonous dead level.'* This particular issue was certainly tackled by Steve Jobs in his meeting with President Obama in 2010 when Jobs attacked America's education system saying it was hopelessly antiquated and crippled by union work rules. *'Until the teachers' unions were broken, there was almost no hope for education reform. Teachers should be treated as professionals, not as assembly-line workers. Principals should be able to hire and fire them based on how good they were,*[3] he said.

Steve Jobs could equally have said the same about the UK education system.

In 1969 the UK Labour Government published the White Paper *In Place of Strife*. The title was a reworking of the book by Aneurin Bevan, *In Place of Fear*. The aim of the proposed act was to curb the power of the trade unions in the UK. It never passed into law basically because of the opposition of the then Home Secretary James Callaghan. It was considered by many that the lack of legislation played a role in the escalation of union disputes and strike action that virtually brought the British economy to its knees in the 1970s.

Capitalism, worker exploitation, profits and state ownership continued (and still continue) to be major concerns within the Labour Party. It was considered by many that further conflict with the unions would lead to electoral defeat. In 1970 the Labour Party was defeated and strike activity continued to rise during the subsequent Conservative Government.

The first legislation to limit union power was the Employment Act of 1980. The Employment Act of 1982, The Trade Union Act of 1984 and the Trade Union and Employment Acts of 1988 followed. The bitter strike over pit closures in 1984 by the NUM ended in their defeat in 1985. It could be argued that Union power in British Industry as practiced from the end of the Second World War ended with that strike.

Whilst manufacturing has diminished drastically during my lifetime, associated legislation and legal services have continued to thrive, a development one suspects, not anticipated by those now defunct Industrial Unions, whose former power appears to have been transferred to Public Sector Unions.

References:

[1] *The Innovative Engineer* published by Morgan-Grampian (publishers) Ltd 1981. Chapter: Scientific Management – The steel man from America was the unacceptable face of work analysis.

[2] *Royal Commission on Trade Unions and Employers' Associations 1965-1968 Report* presented to Parliament by command of Her Majesty June 1968. HMSO.

[3] *Steve Jobs.* Walter Isaacson. Little, Brown Book Group.

D4

MANUFACTURING DECLINE
(Inevitable or neglect?)

During my working life, the UK political view was and apparently still is, that the UK is an advanced industrial power. It is considered that an advanced industrial power is one that has progressed in stages starting with an economy based on agriculture, developing to an economy based on manufacturing and finalising in an economy based upon service industries. It is believed that manufacturing decline is inevitable as productivity increases. The UK view contrasts with that of Germany whose economy is based on manufacturing. Germany it would appear has the view that to be an advanced industrial power requires an economy that is based on manufacturing.

It is not contentious to say that one of the major reasons that the UK became a super power was due to it being the first nation to industrialise. Manufacturing capability and competence was essential to become a major power as was illustrated by the subsequent rise of Germany, USA and Japan. The projected rise of China and India will be dependant upon their manufacturing capability and competence. Manufacturing capability and competence clearly matters.

Following WWII in 1945, the Percy committee report on higher technological education recommended that Colleges of Advanced Technology (CAT's), with the power to award national accredited diplomas and doctorates, with status equal to those of traditional universities, be set up. The proposals met with vigorous opposition from the University Grants

Committee. In 1946 the Barlow report on the supply of scientific manpower was published. The post war government placed greater emphasis on the subject of science than it did on technology and as a consequence the Percy committee recommendations were allowed to wither.

It was not until the publication of the 1956 white paper on higher technological education that the concept of CAT's was re-launched[1].

The above affected me personally as I, at the time, was a pupil at a Lancashire grammar school and along with others was encouraged to take up the subjects of Mathematics, Physics and Chemistry at GCE A-Level.

I left school in 1959 with GCE A-Levels in Mathematics, Physics and Chemistry and entered a five-year sandwich course, which ultimately lead to a Diploma in Technology, awarded by the National Council for Technological Awards. Baron C P Snow, CBE, physicist and novelist, famous for the novel *The Two Cultures*, and ex Government Minister, presented me with the Diploma, which allowed me to use the letters DipTech after my name.

In 1963 a report to the Council for Scientific and Industrial Research (CSIR) titled 'Engineering Design' was published. It was known as the 'Feilden Report', after the chairman Mr G B R Feilden. With the exception of the secretary, all members of the committee were members of the Institution of Mechanical

---

[1] Suggested further reading on the above:

1. *The Audit of War.* Author, Correlli Barnett. Publisher, faber and faber.

2. Image and Status, *engineering* Issue 3, February 1997. Journal of the Engineering Council.

Engineers. On the day the report was published *The Times* Industrial Correspondent commented:

'The vein of trenchant criticism runs all through the report. It is understood that Whitehall only agreed to its publication with reluctance.'

The report stated:

'Every industry is dependant upon engineering for capital plant and equipment; the quality of engineering design is therefore a major factor affecting costs and productivity in all industries including the engineering industries themselves.

'The engineering profession has a lower social and economic status in Britain than in other industrialised countries.

'Technology attracts a lower proportion of the ablest school leavers than science, and, of those who take engineering degrees and enter engineering industry, most are attracted by research and management appointments; very few take up design as a career.'

The above statements are still valid today.

The contents of the report also included the following:

'The system of Government financial control makes it very difficult for the Admiralty to break the normal policy of accepting the cheaper tenders for a contract rather than the best technical solution for the operator's requirements.

'The lowest tender is likely to be based on less research, to allow for less development and to be more prone to failure, and therefore is unlikely to be the best overall solution.

'We were disturbed to learn of the high cost of unreliability in the Royal Air Force – maintenance makes up 50% of the total cost of the Royal Air Force.

'Only rarely, in Universities, are students encouraged to regard their studies as preparatory to a career in industry as designers and producers of goods.

'Some elementary knowledge of production methods and of the use of the product, as well as of principles, is necessary before a student can start to design even the simplest mechanism.

'Scientific problems are assumed to have single solutions: the solutions to engineering problems are almost always compromises.

'The function of a course at university level should be to give the engineer an adequate grounding in the basic scientific principles applied to engineering, to teach him scientific method, to develop his critical faculties and to make him aware of the kind of problems he will face as an engineer.

'We are, therefore, strongly in favour of the 'sandwich' course leading to a first degree or Diploma in Technology for engineers destined to be designers.'

All the above could be regarded as being somewhat critical of the established order of doing things in the UK. The upshot of all this was that the British tradition prevailed. In 1966 the CATs were emasculated into conventional universities. The Council for National Technological Awards (CNTA) was replaced with the Council for National Academic Awards (CNAA) and I subsequently received a certificate from the CNAA awarding me a degree of Batchelor of Science allowing me to use the letters BSc after my name. This development, in conjunction with the 1964 Industrial Training Act (see chapter D3 titled TRADE UNIONS), effectively sabotaged the concept of company sponsored work experience and academic study sandwich courses.What did I think at the time? – I thought what a complete and utter farce the British educational system was in relation to engineering, manufacturing in particular. I also thought how perceptive C Northcote Parkinson was in describing the UK way of doing things in his book *Parkinson's Law*.

The experience did however lead me to understand the way things were, and at the first opportunity I obtained a Diploma in

Management Studies at Strathclyde University whilst working in Scotland.

In all fairness I did manage to earn a reasonable living during my working life and on the whole enjoyed it.

Is manufacturing decline inevitable or due to neglect? It could be argued that manufacturing decline is inevitable if you have Government and institutions staffed by personnel qualified and imbued with a 'classics' outlook, an outlook that has been and still continues to be the case in the UK.

KEEPING WARM
(A need taken for granted?)

Keeping warm is one of mankind's physiological needs. The first basic need of the five hierarchal classes expounded by the psychologist Abraham Maslow.

The coldest winter I recall was in 1947. I can still remember pushing a pram to the local gas works and getting it filled up with coke for 1 shilling (5p). Power cuts were common in the two decades following World War II. The importance of reliable power availability, both industrially and domestically was blatantly obvious.

At the time a career in the power industry seemed a sensible choice to take.

In 1959 I left a Grammar School at 18 with GCE 'A' Levels in Mathematics, Physics and Chemistry and signed up for a student apprenticeship with the British Thomson-Houston company (BTH), a company based in Rugby that manufactured consumer and industrial electrical goods that included machinery and equipment for power generation.

Following graduation in 1963, my first real job was production controller for large steam turbine diaphragms used in 60 MW to 500 MW steam turbine generators, manufactured at AEI Turbine Generator Division, Manchester, (formerly Metropolitan-Vickers Ltd).

In the late 1950s British companies capable of designing and manufacturing large electricity generators included the English Electric Company Ltd (EE), General Electric Company Ltd

(GEC), CA Parsons & Company Ltd, British Thomson-Houston Company Ltd (BTH), and Metropolitan-Vickers Ltd (MV).

Less than 40 years later there were none. The sequence of events that resulted in this situation were as follows:

In 1960 Metropolitan-Vickers and the British Thomson-Houston Company merged to become Associated Electrical Industries (AEI).

GEC acquired AEI in 1967 and EE in 1968.

CA Parsons & Company merged with A Reyrolle & Company in 1968 to form Reyrolle-Parsons.

In 1977, Reyrolle-Parsons merged with Clarke Chapman to form Northern Engineering Industries plc, which in turn was acquired by Rolls Royce plc in 1989.

In 1997, Rolls Royce sold Northern Engineering Industries plc to the German conglomerate Siemens.

In 1989, GEC eventually amalgamated its power generating activities with the French conglomerate Compagnie Générale d' Electricité (CGE) to form GEC Alsthom Ltd ultimately selling its shareholding to a renamed Alstom in 1998.

The demise and loss of ownership of the above companies was explained at the time as the result of much needed rationalisation, allowing the UK to concentrate on service industries.

One such service industry is that of organising and controlling the power stations themselves and the supply of electrical power resulting from them. The Central Electricity Generating Board (CEGB), created in 1957, was made responsible for electricity generation in England and Wales. Following its creation the CEGB was responsible for a massive steam power generation programme. The power stations built were fuelled by coal and atomic energy.

The many miners' strikes, in particular those of 1974 and 1984, coupled with the discovery of oil and gas, helped lead to the reduction and replacement of coal power stations with those powered by gas and oil.

In the late 1960s the British nuclear power programme was the largest in the world. The British nuclear industry started with gas-cooled, graphite-moderated reactors (Magnox). For the second generation of nuclear reactors, the UK persisted with gas cooling technology with advanced gas-cooled reactors (AGRs). France in contrast changed from gas-cooled reactors to water-cooled reactors. The UK cost comparisons were based on political considerations whilst those of France were based on engineering and technical considerations.

In terms of nuclear power it is clear that the UK pursued the wrong technology. Future nuclear stations in the UK will in all probability be based on either the Areva European Pressurised Reactor (EPR) or the American Westinghouse AP1000 Reactor. Whichever of the two is decided upon, the UK contribution will probably be the imposition of our 'unique' expertise in health & safety requirements that will probably ensure further delays and higher costs than would be incurred elsewhere.

The CEGB, run in the main by professional engineers, was broken up to form Powergen (1989), National Power (1990), Nuclear Electric (1990) and The National Grid Company (1990). The CEGB was ultimately disbanded by 2001.

Powergen was taken over by the German company E.ON in 2002.

National Power de-merged into Innogy and International Power in 2000.

Innogy was acquired by the German company RWE in 2002.

International Power was acquired by the French company GDF Suez in 2012.

Nuclear Electric was renamed British Energy in 1995 and was acquired by the French company EdF in 2009.

In short from 1995 when the UK Government sold its remaining shares in what was the CEGB, it took less than seven years for the bulk of the electrical power generating capability in England and Wales to be transferred from UK ownership to German and French ownership. In Scotland, Scottish Power, the larger of the two Scottish energy companies, was taken over by the Spanish company Iberdrola in 2006.

In summary, in 2012 there were six main energy suppliers to the UK market: SSE, British Gas, NPower, EdF, E.ON and Scottish Power. Only the first two were UK owned.

Who? you may ask, has benefited from all these changes with their associated myriad of wheeling and dealing? From an engineering perspective it has certainly not been the UK engineering profession, nor, one suspects, UK plc and the UK taxpayer.

The energy policy of the UK was set out in the 2007 Energy White Paper and the Low Carbon Transition Plan of 2009. In essence the policy is dominated by the perceived need to reduce carbon dioxide emissions as a result of agreeing to the Kyoto Protocol.

The Kyoto Protocol adopted in 1997 is based on the scientific opinion that continued growth in greenhouse gas concentrations caused by human induced emissions will generate high risks of dangerous climate change.

The greenhouse gases concerned are carbon dioxide (CO_2), nitrous oxide (N_2O), methane (CH_4) and sulphur hexafluoride (SF_6). It is worth noting that the most important contributor to climate change is in fact water vapour. Water vapour is not listed on the Kyoto Protocol greenhouse gas list because presumably, technically speaking, it is not a gas. Water vapour does not conform to the gas laws.

Future UK energy policy is based on the Government commitment to reducing CO_2 levels as a result of the belief that man-made CO_2 is responsible for global warming. The Stern report was published to justify this approach by detailing the costs that would be incurred on the supposition that this was so.

The manner in which the report was issued brought to mind the decision made concerning the UK nuclear AGR programme.

To be effective in their work professional engineers deal in compromises based on facts, as opposed to compromises based on beliefs or opinions. One would hope that the Government energy policy would also operate in a similar manner. Facts, unfortunately, no matter how presented are perceived as boring. Facts not only get in the way of beliefs they also suffer the disadvantage of often requiring too much effort in their understanding and application. Beliefs are different, they, like opinions, can and often arouse emotions. Some people are even prepared to kill and die for their beliefs. Below are three beliefs, two of which relate directly to the Kyoto Protocol:

1. An increase in CO_2 from a level of 0.03% to 0.05% in the Earth's atmosphere will have a disastrous effect for mankind.

2. Man made CO_2 is a major cause of global warming.

3. Fairies live at the bottom of your garden.

The implications of believing and acting on the first two beliefs, is having an increasing adverse effect on the cost of generating electrical power in the UK. In recognition of these costs, the Stern Report was commissioned on behalf of the Government to indicate that the adverse costs would be more than offset by the costs incurred if the UK did not act to curb CO_2 emissions.

The belief concerning fairies, improbable as it may seem, was held by Sir Arthur Conan Doyle, creator of Sherlock Holmes. Sir Arthur, a stalwart of British Society and a fervent spiritualist, wrote *The Coming of the Fairies,* in which he defended the authenticity of the world's longest-running photographic hoax, the myth of the 'Cottingley Fairies'. The photographs, taken between 1917 and 1920 by two young schoolgirls purported to show fairies and gnomes cavorting at the bottom of their garden. The photos were eventually published in the *Strand* magazine and caused a sensation. The photos were believed by many influential people to prove the existence of fairies. It was not until 1983, after Geoffrey Crawley, a scientific journalist, had shown beyond doubt that the photos were faked that the girls admitted their deception. "I don't see how people could believe they're real fairies," Frances Griffiths, one of the two perpetrators is reported to have told Crawley when interviewed.

It would appear that fervently held beliefs are difficult to change.

As the subject of UK energy involves political beliefs it is worth considering some beliefs, as opposed to facts, concerning politicians and vice versa. Below are some beliefs that are held concerning politicians:

> Politicians do not like to admit they are wrong.
> Politicians like to appear in control.
> Politicians surround themselves with advisors who reinforce their beliefs.
> Politicians thrive on froth and not on substance.
> Politicians react to public opinion in a knee jerk manner. Rather than tackling the root cause of a problem, a UK politician is more likely to change the name of the problem.
> Politicians not only appear to believe their own 'b*llsh*t', they expect others to believe it too. (In fairness some readers may be thinking that this also applies to the author.)

Politicians' beliefs concerning their constituents, is perhaps best illustrated by quotations attributed to two past American Presidents.

Abraham Lincoln:

'You may fool all of the people some of the time, you can even fool some of the people all of the time, but you cannot fool all of the people all of the time.'

George W Bush:

'You can fool some of the people all of the time, and they are the ones you want to concentrate on.'

In either case there appears to be an awful amount of fooling going on.

The importance of energy within the UK Governments during my lifetime, is illustrated by the changing titles of the Ministries and the Departments that were concerned with the topic:

In 1942 the Ministry of Fuel and Power was formed.

In 1957 the Ministry of fuel and power was renamed the Ministry of Power.

In 1969 the Ministry of Power became part of the Ministry of Technology.

In 1970 the Ministry of Technology was merged with the Board of Trade to create the Department of Trade and Industry.

Following the 1973 oil crisis, the Department of Energy was created in January 1974, formed by taking it from the Department of Trade and Industry.

In March 1974 following the election of the Labour Party, the Department of Trade and Industry was split into the

Department of Trade, the Department of Industry and the Department of Prices and Consumer Protection.

In 1983 the departments of Trade and Industry were reunited.

In 1992 the Department of Energy with many of its functions abandoned, was re-merged back into the Department of Trade and Industry. Those functions that were not abandoned were split between various departments such as the 'Office of Gas Supply', the 'Office of Electricity Regulation', the 'Department of the Environment' and the 'Department for National Heritage.'

In 2005, following the general election the Department of Trade and Industry was renamed the Department for Productivity, Energy and Industry. Less than a week later, following widespread derision, the new department reverted back to the Department of Trade and Industry. (The abbreviation of the new department would have been 'Penis'.)

In June 2007 the Department of Trade and Industry was replaced with the creation of the Department for Business, Enterprise and Regulatory Reform and the Department for Innovation, Universities and Skills.

In 2008 the Department of Energy and Climate Change was created.

In short, it would appear that the generation of electrical power, the source of our most used energy, has been, and continues to be a plaything, expressing the current political whims of the moment. It would also appear to have been, and continues to be run accordingly.

In 2010 the following three events occurred, affecting areas near to where I live that help illustrate the UK attitude and approach to energy.

Firstly the Thanet Wind farm at Foreness Point, comprising 100 wind turbines capable of producing 300 MW was declared open. The event was declared to be the forerunner of more to come. Future plans included the Thames Estuary Wind Farm, the London Array, which, when completed, will comprise 341 wind turbines capable of generating 1000 MW.

Secondly at Kingsnorth power station, a proposed plan of replacing the existing 1,936 MW (4 x 484 MW) coal fired steam generators with 1,600 MW (2 x 800 MW) high efficiency coal fired units was met with massive Greenpeace demonstrations and green camps, whose avowed objective was to close the station down completely. The police were heavily criticised in the media in their efforts to stop the 'Climate-Change' demonstrators occupying the power station.

Thirdly the Government published a list showing preferred nuclear power station sites. The proposed sites did not include Dungeness where currently nuclear power station A is currently being dismantled and where nuclear power station B is currently operational. Dungeness 'A' was capable of producing 438 MW.

In addition to the above three events, Kingsnorth power station (1,940 MW) and Grain oil-fired power station (1,380 MW) will close down by 2015 as neither station have installed flue gas desulphurisation equipment, both stations having opted out of the Large Combustion Plant Directive (LCPD). The closure of Kingsnorth and Grain power stations within five years will result in a loss of 3,320 MW to the National Grid. This loss alone is equivalent to 1,100 wind turbines, three times that planned for the London Array.

In essence, in the area that I now live, 438 MW of nuclear power has been replaced by 300 MW of wind power, and 3,656 MW of legislation driven closures has been replaced by the deferment of the Kingsnorth coal-fired 1600 MW plan, and the proposal of a 1,000 MW wind farm in the Thames Estuary.

In reality, the shortfall in all probability will be met with a combination of importing electricity and the building of gas fired combined cycle generation power plants that will not only operate in their own right but also as a necessary stand by when the wind turbines are idle. The gas will probably be imported, unless UK gas is obtained by the development of existing techniques for extracting gases from the burning of underground coal[1] and the exploitation of shale gas. Developments of both will of course generate the usual objections from the multitude of environmental lobbies that are now an entrenched presence on the UK political scene.

In summary, I dread the thought that as I approach dotage, probably suffering from some form of dementia, I will end up pushing a pram to the local gasworks to get coke to keep warm, having forgotten that gasworks along with all the engineering know-how and facilities associated with getting things designed, made and done in the UK, all ceased to exist in my lifetime.

Looking on the bright side it could be that I will be basking in sunshine with fairies living at the bottom of my garden.

References

[1] Technical Feature. *Professional Engineering*. August 2011. IMechE.

[2] Cover Story. *Professional Engineering*. February 2011. IMechE.

D6

FOSSIL FUELS
(Are their demises exaggerated?)

Carbon dioxide emissions resulting from burning fossil fuels is considered to be a major cause of current global warming. Whether this is true or not, it is a fact that fossil fuels are a finite resource and it would appear logical to ensure that every effort ought to be made in maximising their efficient and effective use whenever they are used. As fossil fuels are a diminishing resource the need for alternative energy sources has become more pressing. The topic of burning fossil fuels is clearly worth investigating.

Burning, or combustion is a chemical reaction in which a substance combines with oxygen to produce heat, light and flame. Most of the energy required by human civilisation currently involves the oxidation of fossil fuels comprising of carbon in the case of coal, and carbon and hydrogen in the case of gas and liquid fuels.

Carbon (C) is converted into carbon dioxide (CO_2), and hydrogen (H_2) is converted into water (H_2O), in the form of steam or water vapour.

Petrol, a distillate from crude petroleum, is basically a mixture of fuels that have the formulation $C_{2n}H_{2n+2}$. A typical fuel could consist of Pentane (C_5H_{12}), 10%; Heptane (C_7H_{16}), 30%; Octane (C_8H_{18}), 35%; Dodecane ($C_{12}H_{26}$), 15% and Benzene (C_6H_6), 10%. The simplest fuel of this type is in fact methane (CH_4), an abundant natural gas.

Bio-fuel, for example ethanol (C_2H_5OH), is considered to be more environmentally friendly than petrol. Brazil uses ethanol produced from sugar cane as a substitute for petrol. The production of ethanol from sugar cane or corn requires land that would otherwise be used to produce food. A farmer growing maize, given the choice between selling his crop for use as a fuel or for food, would sell for the best price. The use of agricultural land for the production of fuel will inevitably raise the cost of food.

Coal, formed by the decomposition of vegetable matter over many millions of years, occurs in large underground deposits. Coal formed the basis of the UK Industrial Revolution. Coal basically replaced both wind and water as a source of energy. Windmills, waterwheels and sailing ships were shown to be hopelessly inferior and inadequate in both an economical and efficiency sense when compared to the use of fossil fuels allied with engineering knowledge and application.

Coal-gas, the source of gas fuel when I was young, was manufactured by the heating of coal in closed iron retorts. The average composition of coal-gas was: hydrogen (50%), methane (30%), carbon monoxide (8%), nitrogen, oxygen and carbon dioxide (8%) and other hydrocarbons (4%). Huge cylindrical gas storage tanks situated near to gas works were a familiar site in my childhood.

Coke, a residue from the production of coal gas was commonly used as a low cost domestic solid fuel.

Water gas, another fuel gas, is obtained by the action of steam on glowing hot coke:

$$C + H_2O = CO + H_2$$
$$C + 2H_2O = CO_2 + 2H_2$$

Water gas can be converted into a liquid fuel by means of the Fischer-Tropsch process or synthesis, which converts the mixture of carbon monoxide and hydrogen into liquid hydrocarbons.

$$(2n+1)H_2 + nCO > C_nH_{(2n+2)} + n\,H_2O$$

For example, if $n = 2$: $5H_2 + 2CO > C_2H_6 + 2H_2O$

The original process was invented in Germany during the 1920s where it was commercialised in 1936. The process was used by both Germany and Japan during World War II. The process is currently used on a large scale at various locations, particularly in South Africa where the process was further developed during the apartheid era. The convenience of liquid fuels, compared to a solid fuel such as coal, could from an engineering viewpoint, result in the Fischer-Tropsch process becoming increasingly attractive, despite the high capital and maintenance costs involved.

Coal, in summary, was and still remains a very valuable and versatile energy resource. It is a ready accessible source of energy.

Notwithstanding the above it would perhaps be instructive to compare the relative merits of petrol, bio-fuel, coal and methane in respect to carbon dioxide emissions.

Chapter D8 titled: 'COMBUSTION DETAILS OF SOME FUELS & RELEVANT COMMENTS', shows the calculations by which the figures quoted below can be checked.

Burning one 1 kg of each of the four fuels produces the following emissions:

Coal: 3.67 kg of carbon dioxide.

Methane: 2.75 kg of carbon dioxide plus 2.25 kg of water vapour.

Petrol: 3.1 kg of carbon dioxide plus 1.4 kg of water vapour.

Bio-fuel: 1.91 kg of carbon dioxide plus 1.17 kg of water vapour.

Burning each fuel to give the same energy output as 1 kg of coal produces the following emissions:

Coal: 3.67 kg of carbon dioxide.

Methane: 1.79 kg of carbon dioxide plus 1.46 kg of water vapour.

Petrol: 2.36 kg of carbon dioxide plus 1.06 kg of water vapour.

Bio-fuel: 2.33 kg of carbon dioxide plus 1.43 kg of water vapour.

In a modern power station, for each comparable unit of electricity generated by coal fired steam turbines, there are 10.50 kg of CO_2 produced, compared to 2.75 kg of CO_2 plus 2.25 kg H_2O for gas turbines (using methane).

For automobiles, on the basis that their respective efficiencies are of the same order, the gas emission comparison using petrol is 2.36 kg CO_2 plus 1.06 kg H_2O, whilst that for bio-fuel is 2.33 kg CO_2 plus 1.43 kg H_2O.

If one is concerned with CO_2 emissions to the exclusion of everything else, coal produces more CO_2 per unit of calorific value when burned, than does methane, petrol or ethanol. For the generation of electricity it can be seen that coal fired power stations produce almost four times as much CO_2 than do gas fired power stations.

If however, water vapour is added to CO_2 to give total 'greenhouse gas' emissions then the resultant emissions for coal and gas become 10.46 kg and 5.0 kg respectively. If the emissions are factored in relation to their 'greenhouse effect', on the basis that water vapour has four times the effect than does CO_2, then the resultant 'greenhouse effect' contribution comparison between coal and gas becomes 10.46 kg for coal and 12.75 kg for gas.

Summarising, if allowance is made for the contribution of water vapour to the 'greenhouse effect' then it could be argued that gas fired power stations are worse than coal fired power stations, dependant upon the weighting given to CO_2 emissions compared to water vapour emissions.

Whilst coal does not produce water vapour upon being burned, it contains impurities such as sulphur, the latter producing sulphur dioxide (SO_2), a major constituent of acid rain. For large coal fired power stations these gases need to be removed by the installation of flue gas desulphurisation equipment in order to conform to the Large Combustion Plant Directive, a European Union directive aimed at reducing emissions of SO_2, N_2O and dust.

Coal, natural gas and oil are all diminishing resources and as such if used for the generation of electricity one would have thought that every effort would be made to ensure that they would be used efficiently by maximising the power obtained for each kilogram burned. Imagine a policy whereby approximately 10% of the electricity generated from a coal, oil or gas fired power station was deliberately used up, without any of it being available for industrial or domestic usage. Imagine also that the cost of supplying the equipment to do this was approximately 50% of the cost of the power station itself. Finally, imagine the cost to both industrial and domestic consumers that such a policy would result in. Such a policy, one would have thought, would not only waste diminishing resources, it would help create conditions for commercial suicide not to mention domestic hardship contributing towards increasing in deaths in winter.

What Government you may ask would contemplate this apparent nonsense? The answer is the UK Government with its CCS (Carbon Capture & Storage) policy.

CCS requires energy, and additional capital to capture, liquefy, transport and store CO_2 from power stations burning fossil fuels in order to reduce levels of man made CO_2 emitted into the atmosphere. The policy is based on the obsession of reducing CO_2 emissions.

It needs to be repeated that water vapour is the most potent greenhouse effect agent contributing three to four times more than CO_2, the second most potent. It is the thermal properties of water, within our atmospheric pressure and a relatively small temperature range, that make water vapour such a potent force in shaping our climate.

The encouragement of policies in which the prime objective is to reduce CO_2 emissions is what one would rationally expect from a country that does not use fossil fuels as a primary energy source. Such a country could, for example, be France where 80% of generated electricity is nuclear. The policy would give such a country a competitive advantage over countries using fossil fuels. The last country one would expect such a policy would be a country using fossil fuels, such as the UK, whose prime objective from an engineering perspective ought to be maximising the efficient use of the fuels themselves.

There is clearly more to the subject of fossil fuels and Government policies associated with their use than meets the eye.

MAN-MADE CARBON DIOXIDE
(A convenient political scapegoat?)

I recall, in my childhood years, family summer holidays in the North West of England that were often spent looking for somewhere to go to avoid the miserable summer weather and persistent rain. The situation does not appear to be any different today, except that the majority of the population do appear to have more choices of where to go to avoid the dismal weather. In going elsewhere there is a viewpoint that the people concerned are contributing to climate change. The subject of 'global warming' has become in some minds the most pressing problem concerning mankind. Our climate is changing, and it is believed that we are the major cause through our emissions of greenhouse gases. The facts about climate change are considered essential to understand the world around us and to make informed decisions about the future. Global warming sceptics are accused of 'cherry picking' and denying the full body of evidence. It is with the above in mind that the following chapter is written.

Imagine watching on TV a Cup Final at Wembley Stadium between Chelsea and Manchester United with a full stadium of 105,000 football spectators, all mixed amongst each other, consisting of:

81,931 dark blue shirted Chelsea fans, (78.03%).

21,998 red shirted Manchester United fans, (20.95%).

976 white shirted Fulham fans, (0.93%).

63 black and white striped shirted Newcastle United fans, (0.06%).

32 pale blue shirted Manchester City fans, (0.03%).

Do you think that you would notice the 32 pale blue shirted Manchester City fans?

Imagine a few years later watching the same Cup Final scenario, but with 16 additional pale blue shirted Manchester City fans replacing 16 red shirted Manchester United fans. Would the 50% increase of Manchester City fans make any difference compared to the previous occasion when they last met? Anyone believing that it would make any difference, never mind noticed, could expect to be ridiculed and the belief that it would make a difference would certainly be regarded as preposterous. If we substitute the Earth's atmospheric gases for the names of the football teams, keeping the same percentage figures used above, then we have the following:

Nitrogen (N_2): (78.03%).

Oxygen (O_2): (20.95%).

Argon (Ar): (0.93%).

Various Gases: (0.06%).

Carbon Dioxide (CO_2): (0.03%).

We are repeatedly informed that an increase of 50% in the levels of CO_2 in the atmosphere will be catastrophic for mankind due to the contribution that increasing levels of CO_2 will have on global warming. The proposition that is clearly absurd in the first instance is now taken for granted as true in the second instance. For this to be true it follows that carbon dioxide possesses properties that are out of all proportion to the other gases comprising the atmosphere.

A property that could be of interest in global warming is the heat retaining ability of the gas concerned. The heat retaining ability of any material is called the heat capacity. Heat capacity is defined as the quantity of heat required to raise the temperature of the material concerned through $1°K$. The heat capacity numerical value is obtained by multiplying the density and specific heat values of the material concerned.

The heat capacity of air is 1284 J/m^3/°K.

The heat capacity of CO_2 is 1649 J/m^3/°K.

The heat capacity of water vapour is 1616 J/m^3/°K.

It can be seen from the above that the heat capacity of CO_2 and water vapour are of the same magnitude, both being higher than that of air. From a thermal viewpoint water has superb qualities. Water is the supreme heat carrier. It has a high specific heat and a very high latent heat, as a result of which it is able to hold a great quantity of heat in a very small bulk or weight.

Latent heat of fusion, (Ice to Water/Water to Ice): 626kJ/kg

Latent heat of evapouration, (Water to Steam/Steam to Water): 2,258 kJ/kg

Heat required to raise water from 0°C to 100°C: 419 kJ/kg

Total heat required to raise water from a solid state, (Ice), to that of a vapour state, (Steam), at normal atmospheric pressure is 3,303 kJ/kg.

Carbon dioxide, in comparison, is a gas at normal atmospheric pressure. The total heat required to raise carbon dioxide from 0°C to 100°C is 326kJ/kg.

It is clear that the thermal properties of water within our atmosphere make water vapour much more a potent force in shaping our climate compared with CO_2. It is also clear that the heat capacity of CO_2 is not the answer to our concern with global warming due to the very small quantities of CO_2 (0.035%) within the Earth's atmosphere.

CO_2, one would think, must possess other properties to explain our concern. Carbon dioxide is considered a greenhouse gas not only because it has a high heat capacity but also because it, (as does water vapour), absorbs infrared radiation.

The 'greenhouse effect', a term now in common use, is the process by which absorption and emission of infra red radiation

175

by gases in the atmosphere warm a planet's lower atmosphere and surface.

The first person to have correctly measured the relative infrared absorptive powers of the atmospheric gases was John Tyndall. John Tyndall was a prominent Irish 19th century physicist. Tyndall, along with a fellow teacher Edward Frankland, moved to Germany in 1848 and enrolled at the University of Marburg to further their education in Science. Frankland was aware that certain German Universities were ahead of any in Britain in experimental chemistry and physics. (British Universities were focussed on classics and mathematics and not laboratory science). When Tyndall returned to England in 1851 he probably had as good an education in experimental science as anyone in England. Tyndall explained the heat in the Earth's atmosphere in terms of the capacities of the various gases in the air to absorb radiant heat (infrared). As a result of his experiments Tyndall concluded that water vapour is the strongest absorber of radiant heat in the atmosphere and is the principle 'gas' controlling air temperature. Absorption by the other gases, which included carbon dioxide and methane, is relatively small.[2.3.]

In essence the most important substance contributing to global warming is not carbon dioxide; it is in fact water vapour. Water vapour contributes between 66% and 85% when including clouds, to the greenhouse effect, far more than carbon dioxide (CO_2) the second most potent greenhouse gas.[1.2.]

What is incontrovertible is that water vapour has a pronounced effect on the Earth's climate.

The Kyoto Protocol does not include water vapour as a greenhouse gas. Water vapour, technically speaking, is not a gas because it does not obey the Gas Laws. The omission of water vapour on the Kyoto Protocol list of greenhouse gases brings to mind the many judicial cases where someone or some organisation, blatantly guilty of a heinous crime, is let off on a legal technicality.

With respect to global warming, as we are apparently not concerned with man-made water vapour on the grounds that there is so much water in the atmosphere that human activities make hardly any difference[2], it could be argued that there appears to be no logical reason why man-made CO_2 caused by burning fossil fuels should cause concern other than using up finite resources.

There are however, other properties that CO_2 possesses that have an effect on global warming. Carbon dioxide as a gas is essential for the production of carbohydrates produced in photosynthesis:

(Solar energy) $+ \quad CO_2 \quad + \quad H_2O \quad = \quad O_2 \quad + \quad CH_2O$

(Solar energy) $+ \quad 6CO_2 \quad + \quad 6H_2O \quad = \quad 6O_2 \quad + \quad C_6H_{12}O_6$

Carbohydrates $[C_x(H_2O)_x]$, play an essential part in the metabolism of all living organisms. Oxygen (O_2) is a by-product of photosynthesis. Carbon dioxide is in effect essential for life. Carbon (C) itself is the building block of all living organisms.

One would have thought that with an atmosphere comprising 0.03% CO_2 there was a danger of there being too little CO_2 never mind too much. If plants had a vote they would undoubtedly agree. Plants do not vote, so on their behalf the question arises:

What is the effect that increasing levels of CO_2 have on plants? There have been many laboratory experiments concluding that increased levels of CO_2 result in increased plant growth, no matter how that plant growth is quantified. For 95% of plants a doubling of CO_2 levels result in a 41% increased growth rate. The increased growth rate for the other 5% is 22%[4]. The practical evidence is that some greenhouse owners artificially elevate the CO_2 levels to triple that in the atmosphere. On this basis it does not seem unreasonable to assume that increase levels of CO_2 in the atmosphere would result in increased levels of food production. Plants do of course require water in addition to CO_2. It should be noted that liquid fossil fuels do emit water (H_2O) in addition to CO_2 upon being burned. It is also not unreasonable to assume that man made CO_2 and H_2O is capable of being absorbed by plants, unless mankind deliberately destroys plants at a rate that prevents this from occurring. In Brazil for example, it has been estimated that 80% of all logging activities is illegal and that if unchecked, 60% of the Amazon rainforest could be wiped out by 2030.

Another interesting property of carbon dioxide is that it has an important function to play in respiration. Blood in the human body requires CO_2 to function properly. When muscles work they burn glucose, ($C_6H_{12}O_6$), and produce CO_2. The excess CO_2 is removed from the bloodstream via the lungs. Breathing produces approximately 1 kg of CO_2 each day per person. (With 15 billion people on the planet, this amounts to an annual total of 5.5 billion tonnes). In engineering terms the human body can be likened to an internal combustion engine. By the very act of being alive, human beings emit both CO_2 and H_2O, as do all engines that burn liquid or gas fuels.

For every 1.5 kg of CO_2 breathed out there is also 0.6 kg of H_2O. (See chapter D8 titled 'COMBUSTION DETAILS OF SOME FUELS & RELEVANT COMMENTS').

The reader may wonder what levels of CO_2 there have been in the past and what connection could be made to a greenhouse effect.

It is believed that during the Cretaceous Period, 135-65 million years ago, when the last dinosaurs, flowering plants and modern insects were on Earth, the CO_2 levels in the atmosphere were 1,700 parts per million (ppm), approximately five times current levels, and the average temperature was 4°C higher than present. We are currently expected to believe that an increase of CO_2 levels by 150 ppm will result in an increase of 2°C. The Cretaceous Period was of course a very long time, too long ago in fact for the creationists and countless others, who believe that the Earth is approximately 10,000 years old and for whom this consideration will be totally irrelevant. To accommodate the creationists and their ilk, and to consider matters nearer home, the 'Skara Brae' settlement on the Orkneys is believed to originate from 3000 to 2500 BC. The settlement was abandoned after 2500 BC when the climate became much colder and wetter. In relatively modern times, the medieval warm period lasted from 950 AD to 1250 AD. The medieval warm period was followed by little ice ages. The worst frost ever recorded in England was the Great Frost of 1683–84 AD, when the River Thames was frozen for two months, and solid ice was reported to have extended for miles off the coast of the southern North Sea.

In considering global warming it would be remiss not to consider the energy sources concerning the Earth itself and also the effect of changes in the Earth's movements regarding the largest of those sources. There is a continuous flow of energy through the Earth's atmosphere and surface. By far the greatest energy source is the Sun. The other two sources, heat from the Earth's interior and tidal energy caused by the gravitational forces of the Sun and Moon, are almost negligible in comparison[5].

The figures are:

Energy from solar radiation: 1.75×10^{17} W
Energy from the earth's interior: 3.24×10^{13} W
Energy from the earth's tides: 3×10^{12} W

To help give a comparison with man's influence, in 1988 the total solar power intercepted by the Earth, 5.52×10^{24}J, was 15,000 times larger than the world's total commercial energy consumption of 3.61×10^{20}J.

If solar radiation increased by a small amount, say 0.01%, this would be greater than the current world's energy consumption.

It would appear logical that any serious attempt to change the Earth's climate would start with changing the amount of solar energy intercepted by the Earth.

Solar radiation management (SRM) techniques proposed include spraying sulphur into the stratosphere in effect mimicking volcanic eruptions[6].

Based on the premise that variations in incoming solar radiation were a fundamental factor controlling the Earth's climate, Milutin Milankovich, a Serbian engineer, during his time as a WWI internee theorised that variations in the eccentricity, axial tilt and changes in orientation of the Earth's rotation axis determined climatic patterns on Earth. The 'Milankovich Cycles' cycles occur at intervals between 26,000 and 41,000 years. The August 2009 edition of *Science* magazine provided evidence that changes in solar insulation (solar radiation energy on a surface) provided the initial trigger for the Earth to warm up after an ice age, with other secondary factors such as greenhouse gases accounting for the magnitude of change. All this of course, does not explain the argument that global warming is currently increasing at a greater rate than in the past, as advocates of global warming repeatedly point out.

Since the early 20th century the Earth's mean surface temperature has increased by approximately 0.8° C of which two-thirds has occurred since 1980.

An obvious question to ask is, what increases in fossil fuel consumption have occurred since 1980? In the event that water vapour has the most pronounced effect on global warming and climate change one would expect disproportionate levels of oil and gas consumption to have occurred from 1980. A comparison of fossil fuel consumption is as follows: [7]

1980 world coal consumption: 3,752,183,000 tons.

2010 world coal consumption: 7,994,703,000 tons. (113% increase).

1980 world oil consumption: 59,928,000 barrels per day.

2010 world oil consumption: 86,952,000 barrels per day. (45% increase).

1980 world gas consumption: 1,400 billion cubic metres.

2010 world gas consumption: 3,200 billion cubic metres. (129% increase).

From the above figures it can be seen that gas consumption has increased the most, followed closely by coal. The International Energy Agency 2012 medium-term coal market report fact sheet states that *'Coal demand is growing everywhere but the United States.'*

Using the above figures, a comparison and magnitude of energy consumption in 2010 for coal, gas and oil respectively was as follows:

Coal 2.61×10^{20} J

$(8.0 \times 10^{12} \text{ kg} \times 32.6 \text{ MJ/kg})$

Gas 1.15×10^{20} J

$(3.2 \times 10^{12} \text{ m}^3 \times 50 \text{ MJ/kg} \times 0.72 \text{ kg/m}^3)$

Oil 1.85×10^{20} J

$(86.95 \times 10^6 \text{ barrels/day} \times 365 \text{ days/annum} \times 159 \text{l/barrel} \times 0.86 \text{ kg/l} \times 42.7 \text{ MJ/kg})$

In short the world's total energy consumption in 2010 from coal, gas and oil was 5.51×10^{20} J.

In the US gas and oil production via 'fracking' has had a major impact on energy costs.

In Japan the reported success in extracting methane from methane hydrates (methane locked in undersea ice), is anticipated to lead to the un-tapping of an energy resource that exceeds the energy content of all oil, coal and other natural gas reserves combined[8].

Returning back to CO_2 emissions, it is currently believed by scientists that approximately 40% of the extra CO_2 caused by human activity since the 1750s has remained in the atmosphere. Of the 60% that has been absorbed it is believed that 30% is absorbed by the oceans. How the other 30% is absorbed on land remains uncertain. The NASA Orbiting Carbon Observatory (OCO) mission was launched in 2009 to help resolve the uncertainties. The spacecraft, unfortunately, crashed into the Pacific Ocean before reaching its planned orbit[9].

Doubts concerning the science associated with global warming itself could not help to be raised upon the disclosure that scientists, at the University of East Anglia, involved in determining the role of human activity regarding CO_2 emissions, were accused of deliberately faking evidence of global warming by manipulating statistics, in what subsequently became known as the 'Climategate' scandal. Further doubts were also raised when the computer models producing the hockey stick curve, that made a visually telling impact in the Al Gore documentary, *An Inconvenient Truth*, were subject to informed criticism. It was also disturbing to read that the US physics professor Harold Lewis resigned from the American Physics Society (APS) citing corruption and the millions of dollars of Government funding at risk concerning global warming in which he quoted the above two examples. (It should be noted that The University of East Anglia and the Pennsylvania State University pardoned both professors Phil Jones and Michael E Mann of any major wrongdoing.)

It can't help be noticed that one certainly does not receive an impartial view from the BBC. The BBC's contribution on global warming invariably starts with the premise that man-made CO_2 is the root cause. BBC coverage of any natural disaster is invariably prefaced with a comment to the effect that this 'could be' or 'may be' linked to global warming, in particular man made CO_2 emissions. Seemingly un-associated documentaries are also subject to aside comments by presenters with the same bias. For example a historical documentary concerning the Scottish Engineers James Watt and James Young included such asides as: 'Letting the carbon genie out of the bottle', and 'No thought of consequences of tomorrow'.

In 2005, on the subject of global warming, the House of Lords economic committee wrote: *'We have some concerns about the objectivity of the IPCC (Intergovernmental Panel on Climate Change) process with some of the emissions scenario and summary documentation apparently influenced by political considerations.'* The committee doubted the high emission scenarios and said the IPCC had played down some positive aspects of global warming. The deliberations of the House of Lords Economic Committee, concerning the topic of CO_2 emissions, were rejected, for political reasons, by the Government of the day and their associated Stern Review.

On a less serious note, it is perhaps worth noting that whilst the concept of 'Carbon Footprint' has entered into common usage, the same cannot be said of 'Water Footprint' or even 'Oxygen Footprint'. If, when told of the billions of tons of carbon dioxide being produced by burning fossil fuels we were also repeatedly told the quantity of oxygen being consumed as a consequence, we would no doubt be subject to demonstrators concerned about the possibility of mankind suffocating due to lack of oxygen. Demonstrators, nowadays more likely to be called activists by the BBC, are not only vociferous, they are committed, ignorant or not. Activists will vote for political parties that pander to their beliefs. The setting up of green camps and continuous demonstrations against coal-fired power stations allied with a sympathetic media, show how entrenched environmental beliefs concerning CO_2 emissions have become.

An example of this belief was shown in the 2008 trial of six Greenpeace protesters who were arrested for causing damage to the Kingsnorth coal-fired power station in Kent. Persuaded by the defence's arguments that the protesters were trying to prevent the greater harm being done by the power station to the climate, the jury acquitted the six.

The trial is referred to in chapter 8 in the book titled *REQUIEM FOR A SPECIES* by the Australian author Clive Hamilton. In the same chapter titled 'Reconstructing a future,' Clive Hamilton suggests that climate change is a direct consequence of governments worldwide not representing the interests of the people, being obsessed with growth fetishism, and allowing themselves to be held in thrall by energy companies. The energy companies themselves, Hamilton suggests, are more interested in commerce than humanities and their executives are at best misguided and self interested.

A totally different approach to the subject of carbon dioxide can be read in the last chapter of the book titled *THE PERIODIC TABLE* written by Primo Levi. The chapter titled 'Carbon,' narrates the life cycle of an imaginary carbon atom explaining that carbon dioxide, the aerial form of carbon constitutes the raw material of life and is the ultimate destiny of all flesh. Primo Levi graphically illustrates the paucity of carbon dioxide in the atmosphere by suggesting that if Italy were air, the only Italians fit to build life would be, as an example, the fifteen thousand inhabitants of Milazzo in the province of Messina.

Clive Hamilton was a former director of the left wing think tank 'The Australia Institute' and was the Australian Green candidate for the federal seat of Higgins where he came second. His views echo those of many who regard opponents to their views on the subject of climate change as being beholden to, and in the pockets of conspiratorial capitalists, particularly those in the oil, petrochemical and energy industries.

Primo Levi was an industrial chemist, a writer and a survivor from Auschwitz concentration camp. Primo Levi was the product of a science education and Clive Hamilton the product of an arts and classics education. An example of the science and classics-arts divide if ever there was one.

The UK Government and institutions are in the main occupied by those who have been educated in the classics and arts. It would not be unreasonable to assume that their views would tend towards the views expressed by Clive Hamilton and not facts as expressed by Primo Levi.

It could be argued that the issue of global warming and the role of CO_2 in it, has gone beyond rational discussion and become entirely political. The role of water vapour and clouds are completely ignored even though they together account for between 66% to 85% contribution to the greenhouse effect. It would appear that there are too many politicians and institutions that have a vested interest in promoting the issue of man-made CO_2 and its role in Global warming whether it is true or not.

Whether we like it or not the minimisation of man-made carbon in the form of the gas CO_2 is now incorporated into UK Government energy policy on the basis that CO_2 is a major cause to global warming. The attractions to politicians are considerable, especially if they surround themselves with advisors reinforcing their beliefs and prejudices. The UK Government for example, can justify the replacement of coal fired power stations with gas fired stations and the resultant rapid exhaustion of our natural gas deposits, by claiming it was all necessary to save the world by reducing CO_2 emissions. Taxes and permit licences such as the 1998 Climate Change Levy and the creation of the world's first national carbon trading scheme in 2004, can be created using the same reasoning. The legislation involved not only keeps politicians busy it also benefits the London Stock Exchange, the legal profession and others. Audits and enforcement procedures need to be initiated and created. Subsidies can be created to encourage what would normally be considered uneconomic or politically based pet projects. Consultancy agencies have additional opportunities to advise their clients on procedures required to mitigate the resultant high costs. Criminals are afforded opportunities to exploit grants and licences such as carbon trading allowances that are created, not to mention the police and fraud agencies that need to be expanded to deal with them. In short a huge bureaucracy can be created with the resultant plethora of regulations, audits, red tape and taxation all based on man-made CO_2. All could be considered examples of state initiated service industries, imposed on consumers whether they like it or not, contributing absolutely nothing in the creation of real wealth, least of all saving the world.

An ability to ask pertinent questions about any topic usually requires some understanding of the topic concerned. In the case of global warming that knowledge would include mathematics, chemistry, physics, biology, thermodynamics and their application in practical terms. In short an education biased towards the applied sciences and technology. It would certainly not be towards the classics.

The leader of the UK delegation on the Kyoto Protocol negotiations was John Prescott, a former left-wing union activist who has a diploma in economics and politics from Ruskin College Oxford and a BSc in economics and economic history from Hull University. In the European Council's commitment that the EU would derive 20% of its energy from renewable resources by 2020, Tony Blair, apparently signed up to the unfeasible target of 32% of our electricity[10]. Tony Blair read Jurisprudence, the theory and study of Law at Oxford University.

The UK Government cabinet position of 'Secretary of State for Energy and Climate Change' was created in October 2008. The first occupant of the post was Ed Miliband, the second occupant was Chris Huhne. Both attended Oxford University and read Politics, Philosophy and Economics. The third and current occupant is Ed Davey who also attended Oxford and also read Philosophy, Politics and Economics. It is after all, as was indicated over 50 years ago in the book *Parkinson's Law*, the way things are done in the UK.

In summary, both carbon and water make up the raw material of life. Carbon dioxide is the aerial form of carbon. It would appear that carbon dioxide is being held accountable for an effect that it is, at worst, only partially at fault. Carbon dioxide has in effect become a very convenient political scapegoat and as such a politically deserving taxable commodity, enabling politicians to tax the very air that we breathe.

References

[1] Water vapour. Greenhouse gas. Wikipedia.

[2] *The Hot Topic*. Gabrielle Walker and Sir David King. Bloomsbury Publishing.

[3] John Tyndall. Wikipedia

[4] *The Direct and Indirect Effects of Increased Carbon Dioxide on Plant Growth*. Thayer Watkins. San Jose State University.

[5] *Mechanical Engineer's Reference Book, Twelfth Edition*. Section 12/3 Alternative energy sources. J Cleland McVeigh. Butterworth-Heinemann.

[6] Protecting the Planet. Ben Hargreaves. *Professional Engineering*. December 2010. IMechE

[7] US Energy Information Administration. International Energy Statistics.

[8] National Geographic Daily News. Re, Japanese state-owned oil and gas company JOGMEC announcement 12 Mar 2013.

[9] Mission to map Earth's CO_2 ends in ignominy as rocket crashes in H_2O. Chris Ayres. *The Times* Feb 25, 2009.

[10] Interview with Sir David King. 'Who's Fuelling the Rise in Your Fuel Bills' BBC Panorama. *Sunday Telegraph* Nov 13, 2011.

COMBUSTION DETAILS OF SOME FUELS & RELEVANT COMMENTS

This chapter is for reference only. It shows how the figures used in chapters D6 and D7 titled FOSSIL FUELS and MAN-MADE CARBON DIOXIDE respectively are calculated. The objective of this chapter is to give the reader an insight into how the quantities of gases are calculated from the burning of fossil fuels

Since reactions occur between integral numbers of molecules and there is conservation of both mass and the number of atoms, molar quantities are used in combustion calculations[1]. A mole of a substance is defined as the weight in grams numerically equal to the substance's molecular weight. The molecular weight is defined as the sum of the atomic weights of all the atoms comprising the molecule.

A molecule is defined as the smallest portion of a substance capable of existing independently and retaining the properties of the substance. An atom is defined as the smallest portion of an element that can take part in a chemical reaction[2]. The atomic weights of the elements used in the following fuel calculations are:

C (Carbon)   – 12
O (Oxygen)   – 16
H (Hydrogen) – 1
N (Nitrogen) – 14

Fuels are usually burned with air, which has the following composition:

21% O_2 + 79% N_2

Nitrogen does not take part in the reaction but it affects the volumetric composition of the products and the combustion temperature.

The products associated with the burning of coal (C) are:

	C	+	O_2	=	CO_2
Chemical Reaction					
Atomic Weights	12	+	32	=	44
Kg/lbs Equivalent	1	+	2.67	=	3.67

Summary: Burning 1 kg of coal produces 3.67 kg of carbon dioxide.

The details associated with burning methane (CH_4) are:

	CH_4	+	$2O_2$	=	CO_2	+	$2H_2O$
Chemical Equation							
Atomic Weights:	(12+4)	+	64	=	(12+32)	+	(4+32)
Total	16	+	64	=	44	+	36
Kg/lbs Equivalent	1	+	4	=	2.75	+	2.25

Summary: Burning 1 kg of methane produces 2.75 kg of carbon dioxide plus 2.25 kg of water vapour.

The details associated with burning octane (C_8H_{18}) representative of petrol are:

Chemical Equation	$2C_8H_{18}$	+	$25O_2$	=	$16CO_2$	+	$18H_2O$
Atomic Weights	(192+36)	+	800	=	(192+512)	+	(36+288)
Total	228	+	800	=	704	+	324
Kg/lbs Equivalent	1	+	3.5	=	3.1	+	1.4

Summary: Burning 1 kg of octane produces 3.1 kg of carbon dioxide and 1.4 kg of water vapour.

The details associated with burning ethanol (C_2H_5OH) or bio-fuel, are:

Chemical Equation	C_2H_5OH	+	$3O_2$	=	$2CO_2$	+	$3H_2O$
Atomic Weights	(24+5+16+1)	+	96	=	(24+64)	+	(6+48)
Total	46	+	96	=	88	+	54
Kg/lbs Equivalent	1	+	2.08	=	1.91	+	1.17

The chemical equation for human breathing, (burning glucose $C_6H_{12}O_6$) are:

Chemical Equation:	$C_6H_{12}O_6$	+	$6O_2$	=	$6CO_2$	+	$6H_2O$ + Energy
Atomic Weights:	(72+12+96)	+	192	=	(72+192)	+	(12+96)
Total	180	+	192	=	264	+	108
Kg/lbs Equivalent	1	+	1.1	=	1.5	+	0.6

Summary: Burning 1 kg of glucose produces 1.5 kg of carbon dioxide plus 0.6 kg of water vapour.

Energy Equivalents for each of the four fuels are:[3]
Coal: 32.6 MJ/kg.
Methane: 50 MJ/kg.
Petrol: 42.7 MJ/kg.
Ethanol: 26.8 MJ/kg.
The weights that would be required to produce the same energy output as 1 kg of coal (ie: 32.6 MJ) for the other three fuels are:
Petrol: 0.76 kg (1x $^{32.6}/_{42.7}$).
Methane: 0.65 kg (1x $^{32.6}/_{50}$).
Ethanol: 1.22 kg (1x $^{32.6}/_{26.8}$).
The efficiency of a modern coal fired power station is in the order of 35%. The efficiency of a combined heat and power modern gas fired power station is in the order of 65%. The weight of coal to produce its own energy equivalent, (32.6 MJ), in a modern power station is therefore 2.86 kg ($^1/_{0.35}$), and that for methane is 1 kg ($^{0.65}/_{0.65}$).
In terms of emissions it follows that for the same energy output the comparison between coal and methane gas is:

Coal: 10.50 kg CO_2 (2.86 x 3.67).

Methane: 2.75 kg CO_2 (1 x 2.75) + 2.25 kg H_2O (1 x 2.25).

In terms of automobiles assuming the efficiency is the same for both bio-fuel and petrol, it follows that the emission comparison is:

Petrol: 2.36 kg CO_2 (0.76 x 3.1) + 1.06 kg H_2O (0.76 x 1.4).

Bio-fuel: 2.33 kg CO_2 (1.22 x 1.91) + 1.43 kg H_2O (1.22 x 1.17).

References

[1] *Introduction to Internal Combustion Engines.* Richard Stone. Macmillan Publishers Ltd. 1985.

[2].*A Dictionary of Science.* Penguin Reference Books. Third Edition 1964.

[3.]*Automotive Handbook.* Bosch. 2nd Edition.

THE SKY IS THE LIMIT
(So far but no further?)

One childhood Christmas present that I still possess is a book that I received in 1948 titled, *The Children's Own Treasure Book,* published by Odhams. The book contents include classic stories, poems, nature articles, puzzles, hobbies and science articles. In the book are two consecutive articles. The first, written by the Astronomer Royal, Sir Harold Spencer Jones is titled 'Shall we really fly to the moon?' the second, written by A E Woodman is titled 'How a jet engine works'.

The first article suggests that rocket propulsion, as shown by the WWII German V2 rocket, made possible the feasibility of escaping the Earth's gravitational pull. The problems in designing and constructing a rocket ship capable of flying to the moon were considered immense, as would the voyage itself. The article concluded that in the event that explorers landed on the moon, they would, in all probability, be marooned there far beyond human aid. The Astronomer Royal concluded that in his view, should all the difficulties be overcome, a voyage around the moon would be well worth the risks involved, in order to gain knowledge of the hidden part of the moon.

It was clear that the Astronomer Royal did not believe in the possibility of space flight. The same could be said about his successor Richard van der Riet Woolley, who on taking his position in 1956 in answer to a press question on space travel said, "It's utter bilge." One year later Russia launched Sputnik1.

The second article shows a cut-away view of a jet engine, a sketch of one of the combustion chambers and a sketch of a Gloster Meteor jet airplane. The article is written in both a factual and inspirational manner explaining the advantages of the jet engine compared to the piston engine. It suggests that the sound barrier would be broken using a jet engined aircraft. The article ends with comments on future developments that include a Vickers-Armstrong jet fighter, a de Havilland swept wing research jet aircraft (de Havilland DH 108 Swallow), and, from the authors perspective the most interesting of all, the Armstrong-Whitworth AW-52 which is described as an ingenious twin engined big mail plane with a wingspan of 90 feet. A sketch of a huge wing with four engines is also shown to give the reader some idea of how a future giant jet-propelled airliner would look. (A larger version of the Armstrong-Whitworth AW-52.) Readers who may be unaware of this plane can see a newsreel and flight comments taken at the time on the website YouTube.

A few years later when I was 12, I, along with like-minded friends used to cycle to Barton Aerodrome to watch Spitfires, Hurricanes and de Havilland Moths taking off and landing. These planes were of course not as exciting to watch as their jet successors, the Gloster Meteor and the de Havilland Vampire, not to mention in the larger English Electric Canberra bomber. To view these planes taking off and landing I had to cycle to Manchester Ringway Airport, which I did when I was 13.

At that time I read copies of *Flight* and *The Aeroplane* magazines whose contents had articles concerning all types of military airplane developments including German aircraft of WWII.

As schoolboys we often had arguments regarding what we perceived to be the relative merits of various aircraft, for example:

On the basis that the UK engineer Frank Whittle invented and developed the jet engine, how had Germany developed theirs? In particular, how had Germany beaten the UK in the use of the jet engine in WWII?

Which was the better jet fighter in WWII? The Messerschmitt 262 or the Gloster Meteor?

Why had the USA broken the sound barrier before the UK?

Why was the MIG-15 so superior to anything that the UK and USA had at the start of the Korean War?

Sixty years later one can only ponder with incredulity the answers to the above questions.

The first patent for the use of a gas turbine powering an aircraft, was filed in 1921 by Maxime Guillaume. His engine was an axial-flow turbojet.

In 1922 the US Bureau of Standards was authorised to publish Report No.109 titled *Jet Propulsion for Airplanes*, as a technical report to the US Subcommittee on power plants for aircraft. The report concluded that propulsion by the reaction of a simple jet *cannot* compete in any respect with airscrew propulsion at such flying speeds as are now in prospect.

In 1926 Alan Arnold Griffith published *An Aerodynamic Theory of Turbine Design* leading to experimental work at the Royal Aircraft Establishment (RAE).

In 1928 Frank Whittle formally submitted his jet engine ideas to his RAF superiors and after developing them submitted his first patent in 1930.

In 1935 Whittle could not afford to pay the £5 patent renewal fee and it was allowed to lapse. In Germany, in the same year, Hans von Ohain started work on a design similar to that of Whittle and introduced the concept to the aircraft industrialist Ernst Heinkel who immediately saw the potential.

In late 1935 two former acquaintances of Whittle formed a partnership and introduced Whittle to two investment bankers, which ultimately lead to the creation of Power Jets Ltd in January 1936. Whittle was given the title 'Honorary Chief Engineer and

Technical Consultant'. Whittle needed permission to work outside the RAF and was allowed to work on the design as long as it was for no more than six hours a week.

With the Air Ministry showing no interest and with no manufacturing facilities of their own, Power Jets entered an agreement with steam turbine manufacturers British Thomson-Houston Ltd (BTH) to build an experimental engine facility on their Rugby premises.

When Power Jets was formed, the Chairman of the Aeronautical Society, Henry Tizard asked the Air Ministry for a report on the Power Jet design. The request was passed to A A Griffith who earlier in 1929 had declared Whittle's design as impracticable. The report was not received back until March 1937. The upshot was that the committee decided to fund the efforts of A A Griffith, who had started construction of his own turbine design, and not those of Whittle.

Power Jets managed to continue with private funding and successfully ran the Whittle engine in April 1937. At this point Tizard recognised the engine as being far superior to any other engine he had seen, and managed to persuade the Air Ministry to fund development with a £5,000 contract. Before the Air Ministry funds were made available one year later in 1938, BTH had already decided to provide funding of £2,500 in addition to moving the Whittle facility from Rugby to more suitable premises at their nearby underused Ladywood foundry premises at Lutterworth.

In the intervening period, Heinkel in Germany ran their first jet engine in September 1937.

The arrival of the Ministry funds in March 1938 meant that Power Jets were subject to the Official Secrets Act making it virtually impossible to obtain further private equity. Following a visit from the Air Ministry in June 1939, Power Jets were able to run their engine for 20 minutes, which convinced the Director of

Scientific Research, D R Pye of the importance of the project. This resulted in the Air Ministry agreeing to buy the engine, loaning it back, injecting further cash and placing an order for a flyable version, the Whittle W1.

In August 1939, one month before war was declared the German Heinkel HE 178 had its maiden flight and became the world's first jet plane.

When war was declared Power Jets had ten on its payroll, and was a similar size to A A Griffith's operations at the RAE and Metropolitan-Vickers.

In August 1940 the German BMW 003 axial-flow turbojet engine was run and in October 1940 the first prototype of the German Junkers Jumo 004 turbojet engine was also run, the latter ultimately becoming the world's first turbojet engine in production and operational use.

In January 1941 Whittle, disillusioned with BTH contracted the manufacture of his engine to the Rover Car Company.

In April 1941 the Gloster E28/39 powered by the Whittle W1 engine flew for 17 minutes reaching a speed of 340 mph. Within a few days the aircraft was reaching 370 mph at 25,000 feet (7,600 m), a speed exceeding the performance of contemporary Spitfires. Whittle's work caused a revolution within British engine manufacturing as nearly all engine companies started crash courses endeavouring to match Power Jets.

In June 1941 the Air Ministry decided that Rover would produce the engine and that Power Jets would be a research company only.

In January 1942 Rolls-Royce contacted Whittle.

In July 1942 the Messerschmitt 262 had its first flight powered by jet engines.

In early 1943 Rolls-Royce took over the production of the Whittle engine from Rover by exchanging its tank engine factory with the two Rover jet plants.

During a demonstration of the Gloster E28/39 to Winston Churchill in April 1943 Whittle proposed to Stafford Cripps that all jet development be nationalised as his company had been funded with private investors only to see production contracts go to other companies. Nationalisation was the way to repay those debts to ensure fairness. Cripps decided that the best solution was to nationalise Power Jets only and incorporate Power Jets into a Government owned establishment.

In June 1943 the German Arado Ar 234 had its maiden flight to become the world's first operational jet powered bomber.

In October 1943 The Miles Aircraft company was chosen by the Air Ministry and the Royal Aircraft Establishment (RAE) to produce a jet powered aeroplane capable of flying over 1,000 mph in level flight and capable of climbing to 36,000 feet in 1.5 minutes. The objective was to deal with the perceived threat of the Messerschmitt Me 262 and the Messerschmitt 163, a rocket-powered fighter aircraft that set a new world speed record of 624.2 mph (1,004.5 km/hr) in October 1941. The 1,000 mph supersonic speed requirement was a mistranslation of an intercepted communication of 1,000 km/h.

In December 1943 the Directors of Power Jets were informed that the Treasury would not pay more than £100,000 for their company.

In January 1944 Whittle was awarded the CBE and the Ministry made a final offer of £135,000 for Power Jets, refusing arbitration on the matter. The offer was reluctantly accepted. Two major individual shareholders received £46,800 each for their shares. Frank Whittle received nothing as he had already offered to surrender his shares. Whittle met with Cripps and objected to the manner in which the nationalisation process was being carried out.

On 28 March 1944 Power Jets was renamed Power Jets (Research & Development) Ltd with H Roxbee Cox as chairman and Whittle as Chief Technical Officer.

In April 1944 the Messerschmitt 262 became the world's first operational jet-powered aircraft. It was one of the most advanced aviation designs in operational use during World War II and was faster and better armed than Allied fighter aircraft, including the Gloster Meteor.

In July 1944 the Gloster Meteor entered service with the RAF.

In 1944 the design work on the Miles M52 had progressed to the stage that Miles were instructed to build three prototypes.

In late 1944 the Air Ministry signed an agreement with the Americans to exchange high-speed research data. The American Bell Aircraft Company was given access to drawings and research on the M52. Miles were unaware that Bell Aircraft had already started on the construction of their own designed rocket powered supersonic aircraft. No data was received in exchange because the US reneged on the agreement.

At the end of WWII the Russians seized most of Germany's aircraft industry along with their plans, prototypes, research and designs.

In February 1946 when the first of the three Miles M52 prototypes was almost completed and a test programme had been initiated with the intention of achieving Mach 1.07 by the end of the year, the project was cancelled by Sir Ben Lockspeiser, the Director of Scientific Research.

In April 1946 the first Soviet turbojet fighter, the MiG-9, had its maiden flight using a pair of reverse-engineered German BMW 003 engines. In the same year Soviet designers, impressed with the superior Rolls Royce Nene engine, suggested to Stalin that they should buy jet engines from the British, Stalin is reported to have said, "What fool will sell us his secrets?" The

British Government, in particular the Minister of Trade, Sir Stafford Cripps, a Marxist and the wartime Ambassador to the Soviet Union willingly provided technical information and a licence to manufacture the Rolls Royce Nene. The Rolls Royce Nene engine was subsequently reverse engineered and produced as the Klimov RD-45 and was used to power the MiG-15, a swept wing fighter that bore an uncanny resemblance to the German Focke-Wulf Ta 183, a proposed successor to the Messerschmitt Me 262. The MiG 15 achieved fame in the Korean War and is believed to have been the most widely produced jet aircraft made. (18,000 compared with 4,000 Gloster Meteors).

Rolls Royce later attempted to claim £207 million in licence fees.

In July 1946 Power Jets R&D Ltd was merged with the gas turbine division of RAE to form the National Gas Turbine Establishment (NGTE) at Farnborough. A disillusioned Whittle along with 16 Power Jet Engineers resigned. Whittle, his invention given to Rolls-Royce and de Havilland to produce, and his company limited to development and testing work suffered a nervous breakdown.

In 1947, the year that the American Bell X-1 first broke the sound barrier, Miles Aircraft Ltd went into receivership. Its aircraft assets were acquired by the Handley Page Aircraft Co Ltd.

The saga of Whittle and Power Jets is worth detailing because it helps illustrate the difficulties associated with patents, private finance, Government funding, design, research, development, manufacturing, Government departments with their vested interests and bureaucracy, and the potential stultifying effects of the Official Secrets Act.

The experiences obtained at Power Jets by G. B R Feilden, who joined Power Jets as an engineer graduate straight from Cambridge, and H Roxbee Cox were clearly shown twenty years later in *Engineering Design,* a report submitted in June 1963 by H

Roxbee Cox, Chairman of the Department of Scientific and Industrial Research to The Rt Hon Viscount Hailsham Q C, Lord President of the Council and Minister for Science.

The report, subsequently known as the Feilden Report, was the result of a committee appointed:

'To consider the present standing of mechanical engineering design in relation to the United Kingdom engineering industry and practice overseas; and to recommend any changes which are likely to result in improved engineering design of British products, including in particular changes in education and training.'

Some extracts of this report can be read in chapter D4 titled 'MANUFACTURING DECLINE'.

Footnote:

In September 2012, BBC Four showed a two part series titled *Jet! When Britain Ruled the Skies* in which it stated, in a condescending manner, that Rolls Royce sold the Nene engine to the Russians. No mention was made of the UK Government involvement. The same programme also stated erroneously, that the English Electric Canberra was the world's first jet bomber.

References:

The Children's Own Treasure Book. Odhams Press Ltd. 1947.
The Quick and the Dead. W A Waterton. Frederick Muller Ltd. London.1956.
Engineering Design. Department of Scientific and Industrial Research. HMSO 1963.
Frank Whittle. Invention of the Jet. Andrew Nahum. 2004. ISBN 1 84046 538 7.
Empire of the Clouds. James Hamilton-Paterson. 2010. ISBN 978-0-571-24795-0.
The Encyclopaedia of Aircraft of World War II. 2004. ISBN 978-1-904687-83-2
Wikipedia.

Section E

REFLECTIONS REGARDING WORK

'There are three ways by which an individual can get wealth - by work, by gift and by theft. The reason why the workers get so little is that the beggars and thieves get so much.'

Henry George
1839-1897

CAR PARKING
(Service, racket or work experience?)

In the early 1960s I occasionally watched the local soccer team when they played at home. I occasionally also watched them when they played away matches against any one of the many nearby soccer teams who at that time all played in Division 1.

One Saturday afternoon I travelled in my car with some friends to Maine Road Stadium to watch our team play Manchester City. I found a suitable location in a back street near to the stadium and parked my car. As I was leaving my car, a small street urchin approached me and said something along the lines: "Do you want me to look after your car Mister?" I interpreted his question to mean something along the lines: 'If you don't give me some money there will be a few scratches on your car, or possibly your tyres may be deflated upon your return.' I responded to his question and said something along the lines: "Yes young man, you look after my car and here is a shilling, paid in advance, to make sure you do." I returned to my car after the match and found it to be exactly as I had left it. The young urchin had performed a service. I also had a choice in the matter of paying, or not paying, for his so called service. A first question arises: 'Was that urchin performing a service or was he participating in a racket?' A second question arises: 'If the urchin was participating in a racket, which I suspected he was, why, as a socially responsible citizen, did I not report him to the authorities?'

Nowadays, if I wish to park my car anywhere in the back streets of a town or city, I am invariably faced with either parking meters or a combination of white and yellow lines patrolled by traffic wardens. There is no question of a service being provided, as there is as much chance of my car being damaged as there was in the early 1960s. I am in fact faced with a racket. A question arises: 'Why, as a socially responsible citizen, do I not report this racket to the authorities?'

It is now clear to me that that 1960s' young urchin was participating in a work experience programme. He not only offered much better value to his customers than that offered by the current system, he also did not require a huge bureaucracy in which to operate.

Unlike manufacturing industries, too many service industries force their services on consumers whether the consumer wants them or not. They are in fact legalised rackets.

FINANCIAL SERVICES
(Can you trust anybody with your money?)

In the early 1960s, my first involvement with the financial service industry was with a local Cooperative Insurance Company (CIS) agent who persuaded me to take out a 'with profits endowment policy' for £1,000, payable at the end of 20 years. I was aware at the time that should I have cashed in before 20 years had elapsed, I would not have received much money back. I was also aware that only one in four people actually lasted the course so to speak. The incentive to last the course, and retain the policy, was the terminal bonus that would be paid on maturity. I envisaged at the time that I would be able to treat myself to a Jaguar saloon car when the policy matured. When the policy did pay out, the Jaguar was out of reach but I could have purchased a Mini. The policy did however serve its purpose. I obtained my first house and subsequent houses using that, and other similar policies, to act as security against the building society mortgage on which I paid interest only. In short the currently much maligned endowment policies served me well.

What became noticeable as I became older were the number of financial companies who offered to buy endowment policies from individuals who wished to cash in their policies before the maturity date; namely from those three out of four endowment policy holders. It was clear that the financial companies concerned were offering more to the individuals, than were the companies who issued the policies.

This development concerned me, as I realised that the bonus payable to me on maturity would inevitably be less than it otherwise would be, as the purchasing financial companies too, would hold their cheaply purchased policies until maturity, in order to get the terminal bonuses. In short it could be argued that endowment policies had become a racket within the financial industry itself.

Agents who sold endowment policies were paid commission. This in itself offered opportunities to some unscrupulous types. A business acquaintance once told me of a relative of his who 'sold' endowment policies to tramps who lived underneath the arches in London. His relative made up fictitious addresses, paid the monthly instalments himself, and upon receiving his commissions left the companies concerned at a time of his choosing. This behaviour may strike the reader as an example of unprofessional, unethical and fraudulent conduct. With hindsight that relation of his was ahead of his time, as similar activities developed into sub prime loans that culminated into the financial crash of 2008, the consequences of which we are still living with today.

Insurance, a major and necessary financial service is interesting. It must be difficult to keep a business afloat where, for example, the number of claims for stolen Rolex watches exceeds the number of Rolex watches actually built. On the other hand it must be easy to be profitable selling life insurance where the life expectancy of the recipient exceeds that of the product coverage.

The first financial scandal I was aware of was that of the Fire Auto & Marine Insurance Company (FAM), set up by Emil Savundra. FAM undercut the established motor insurance companies of the day and ultimately collapsed. The basic reason for the failure was that the company's income could not keep pace with the claims and the lavish lifestyle of its founder. Over

400,000 motorists were affected. Savundra was one of the first controversial businessmen to use UK libel law to prevent magazines such as *Private Eye* from publishing damning revelations. He was jailed in 1968 and released in 1974. He, along with his supporters, probably thought he was a victim of what later became termed 'institutional racism.' Some were no doubt prejudiced against him because of his born name – Michael Marion Emil Anacletus Pierre Savundranayagam. Matters were not helped by the disclosure that days before the collapse of FAM he sold his shares to his directors at FAM the chief of whom was a certain Stuart de Quincy Walker. (Selling them to Fred Bloggs would not have had the same panache.)

There have been many scandals since. They are all invariably based on taking money up front with promises to be paid back with interest, in the future. Most are in effect Ponzi schemes akin to pyramid selling, both of which are illegal. The largest Ponzi scheme exposed to date is that perpetrated by Bernard Madoff who, at the time of writing, is currently in jail in the USA for defrauding $65,000,000,000 from his clients who included individuals and pension funds. As was disclosed by the late Aneurin Bevan, the UK State pension scheme is an example of a Ponzi scheme. Those lucky to be in the top portion of the pyramid will not suffer, but those further down the pyramid certainly will. It should be noted that the UK state pension scheme has not yet been declared illegal and that there are exceptions to most rules.

In the 1980s, after being repeatedly inundated by my bank and others, to obtain loans for items that I neither needed nor wanted, I approached my bank and asked for a loan of £250,000 in order that I could buy a manufacturing company that had £50,000 in the bank, a turnover in excess of £1,000,000, all bills paid, and was the owner of freehold and leasehold properties in London. The owner was well past retiring age. He was both sharp and lucid but had cancer. His son had been educated at Oxford and had no interest in the business. I thought at the time the problem would be my wife, but it turned out to be the bank. The bank would only lend me money to the value of my house, which at the time was worth £70,000. The bank would loan me £250,000 or even more, provided I could first persuade the owner to hand over the company to me before giving me the loan. A catch-22 situation if ever there was one. The interesting thing about the owner was that he would not do a deal with an accountant.

The experience did bring to mind the saying: 'Banks will give you money that you don't need, and not give you money when you do need it.'

Moving around the country I had more than my share of dealing with estate agents. The exception was in Scotland, where interestingly, house sales and purchases were the business of solicitors via solicitor property centres.

In the 1980s the banks and large insurance companies bought and re-branded many estate agencies. The reason given at the time was this would benefit customers by offering an integrated service involving loans, mortgages and insurance. The deals coincided with a boom in property prices at the time, which came to an abrupt end when the then Chancellor of the Exchequer removed mortgage tax relief benefits associated with spouses. The property market collapsed. The banks and insurance companies subsequently had liabilities instead of assets, and re-sold their purchases back to the original owners at knock-down prices. The banks and insurance companies lost millions of pounds as a result. The experience didn't stop the banks involving themselves in the next property boom, which ended in 2008, helping to cause the biggest economic crisis since the great crash of 1929.

The first time I invested directly in shares and unit trusts was during the period when privatisation was in full swing. I replied to an advertisement in the paper for a unit trust fund that I intended to help supplement my future pension by using it under a tax umbrella that at the time was known as a Personal Equity Plan (PEP). I was somewhat annoyed to find out later that had I used a well known stockbroker or independent financial service provider and asset management specialist, I would have obtained more shares of the fund for the same amount of money. In simple terms the fund I bought direct, cost me more than if I had bought it from the stockbroker. The stockbroker clearly made enough as they still have a thriving business.

It would appear that the opportunity of making money in the financial service industries is relatively simple and easy. Money is made by extracting it at source before the proceeds of its investment has been made apparent.

Imagine if you, the reader, at your first interview, had said something along the lines of:

"Employ me, I'm good looking, intelligent and hardworking; my mother says so. In addition to these assets I believe that I will earn £2 million in my lifetime and I want you to give me 10% upfront before I start working for you. Oh, and by the way, I won't guarantee to keep working for you. How about it?"

For a post in industry you would certainly have been shown the door, whether you were good looking or not. For a post in financial services you may well have been shown the door, not because you were not good looking, but because you were not brazen enough. It would appear to be the norm to be paid up front in the financial world. The Earth itself can be promised in the future whilst one takes an immediate down payment in hard cash. One obtains commission and bonuses up front for arranging deals in multimillion takeovers not withstanding the actual outcome of those deals. Licences and legal permission notices can be restricted, thereby creating artificial demands and subsequent high payments to those successful in obtaining them.

Best of all one can pay oneself unlimited salaries and bonuses because one can. (To be fair, this last sentence doesn't just apply to the financial world.) The word 'shyster' does come to mind when one looks at the activities of too many individuals operating in the financial service industry.

The reader may ask: "What views does the UK Government hold with respect to the financial services industry?" A report by the UK National Defence Association (UKNDA) quoted a senior economic advisor to Gordon Brown as saying:

"Defence, aerospace, manufacturing and engineering have no real value to us. Only high-quality professional services and the City of London have any real value and they should be supported at all costs. The rest of the country can be turned over to tourism."

The UKNDA report previewed in the *Daily Telegraph* March 2, 2009, was written by Tony Edwards, a former Head of Defence Export Services at the Ministry of Defence, who said that he was not at liberty to disclose the identity of the official concerned.

The comments were made before the collapse of Northern Rock and were made public after the Government's decision to press ahead with a £1.3 trillion bail out of the banking sector whilst doing little to support industry[1]. We can all do with money up front, even HM Revenue & Customs (HMRC).

Can you trust anybody with your money?

References:

[1] Top Brown advisor 'said only the City was worth supporting'. The *Daily Telegraph* March 3, 2009.

ACCOUNTANTS
(Should they run business?)

An accountant is someone who keeps or inspects accounts. An understanding of cost control is essential for any manager in any organisation, or so one would hope and believe. An accountant is clearly a person suitable for such a task.

There are however, some concepts and perceptions that need to be aired.

The question, 'what is the sum of two plus two?' If posed to an engineer and an accountant, would probably result in 'four', from the former, and 'anything you want to make it', from the latter. A cost effective idea or project from an engineer, expressed in mathematical terms if shown to another engineer would probably be approved. The same project shown to an accountant would probably be rejected on the grounds that there was a fiddle going on that the accountant didn't understand. In the event of cost savings being necessary, an accountant would probably look at closing down departments or, in the case of a large organisation, whole factories. An engineer would probably look at improving the process. It may occur to the reader that if closing departments or factories in a large organisation saves money, then logic would suggest that closing down the whole organisation would save even more. In the event of a fire outbreak, an accountant would probably encourage it, whereas an engineer would probably try to put it out. I will leave it to the imagination of the reader as to why this may be considered so.

In 1936 Britain was preparing for war. The Government, harassed by the opposition over the cost of rearmament, pronounced that it would strictly control the armament manufacturers from making excessive profits. The manner in which the Air Ministry achieved this was with the introduction of an ITP (Instruction To Proceed) document. The ITP document in effect said that the recipient might start work and would be paid something some day, after Government accountants had had time to investigate their business. The recipients quoted fixed price would be taken as a maximum. Government accountants were to have full access to all costs of their business and would make their own estimate of overheads properly chargeable to the contract, and then announce the price that the Government would pay. The Aircraft Industry, being dependent for their existence upon Government orders had no option but to accept contracts on these lines, and then start negotiations to eliminate the initial absurdities of the standard ITP form. The Automobile Industry, in comparison, was not wholly dependant upon the Air Ministry for orders.

An aircraft manufacturing company Airspeed Ltd had designed and adapted its aircraft to accept radial engines that had a high power to weight ratio. The engines were technically superior to any other British engine in its power range. The Nuffield Motor Car Organisation manufactured the engine, and had devoted considerable effort to its development. After considerable negotiation by Lord Nuffield's aero engine sales manager, the company received an invitation to tender for 200 engines for installation in aircraft that the Government were proposing to buy from Airspeed Ltd.

The price quoted on a basis of £ per hp (horse-power) was much lower than those engines of competing companies. The Air Ministry responded by issuing an ITP.

Lord Nuffield studied and noted all the provisions contained within the ITP and concluded that it would have meant a reorganisation of the company's offices and the engagement of an army of chartered accountants. The Nuffield Organisation had spent £200,000 upon the Wolseley Aero Engine and had in effect been rewarded with suspicious nonsense. The ITP form was sent back to the Air Ministry. In September 1936 Lord Nuffield stopped production of the engine without notice, and the aero division of the Nuffield Organisation was closed down. It was a disaster both for Airspeed Ltd and Britain[1]. Lord Nuffield had considered it better to sell motor vehicles for cash to the Admiralty and the War Office, who both retained normal methods of buying and selling. The demise of the Wolseley Aries 111 or AR9 nine-cylinder air-cooled radial aero engine[2] could be considered a practical example illustrating the difference in approach to industry between accountants and engineers.

It is a difference that did not change one iota during my career in industry.

My career started in 1959 as a student apprentice with the British Thomson Houston Co Ltd (BTH), on a five-year sandwich course.

In 1960, AEI (Associated Electrical Industries Ltd) was formed with the amalgamation of BTH, Metropolitan Vickers and Edison-Swan.

In 1965, I left AEI and continued to keep an interest in its subsequent fortunes.

In 1967, AEI was taken over by General Electric Company plc (GEC).

In 1968, GEC merged with English Electric Company Ltd.

In 1979, GEC acquired Yarrow Shipyards.

In 1989, GEC created GEC-ALSTHOM on a 50/50 basis with CGE of France (Compagne General d'Electrique).

In 1990, GEC acquired part of Ferranti.

In 1995, GEC acquired Vickers Shipbuilding.

In 1996, Arnold Weinstock, after a period of 36 years at the helm of GEC, retired to become Chairman Emeritus. He was replaced, with Government and City backing, by George Simpson.

In 1998, GEC sold part of its share of GEC-ALSTHOM to ALSTHOM, who subsequently dropped GEC from its title to become ALSTOM.

In 1999, GEC was renamed Marconi.

In 2001, Marconi collapsed and George Simpson was fired.

Arnold Weinstock, an accountant, knighted in 1970, had in the space of 36 years, taken a company with a turnover of £100 million in 1960, to a company with a turnover of £11 billion in 1996.

The growth of GEC was accomplished by a combination of factory closures, shrewd amalgamations and deals. GEC under Weinstock was controlled by strict budget reporting procedures. In 1983 GEC was a major power in British industry and was the UK's largest private employer with 250,000 employees. (By comparison, in 2010 Tesco was the largest UK private employer with approximately the same number of employees, dwarfed by the UK's largest employer, the NHS, which employed over 1,400,000 employees.)

In the space of five years, George Simpson, Weinstock's successor, also an accountant, transformed GEC, a company valued at £35 billion, and created a company facade worth £150 million at the time of his departure. George Simpson, who was made a life peer in 1997, presided over the largest collapse in British corporate history. Arnold Weinstock, described by the Guardian newspaper as 'Britain's premier post-second-world-war industrialist' died in 2002 having seen the destruction of his lifetime's work, the destruction of his pension holding in GEC shares, and a multi-million pound pay off given to his successor[3].

In 1976, two engineers in the USA sold a second-hand Volkswagen bus for $1500 and a HP 65 programmable calculator for $250. They created a company that they called Apple Computer[4]. The two engineers were Steve Jobs and Steve Wozniak. In 2011 Steve Jobs died. At the time of his death Apple had become the world's second largest company worth about $350 billion. Apple's growth was powered by Steve Jobs in spite of having been fired in 1987 and subsequently reinstated in 1996.

In 2010 *Fortune* magazine, in conjunction with Hay Group management consultants, reported that Apple had won the most admired company award for the third time in succession with the highest profit margin ever. The reason for this was considered to be that Apple had single-handedly changed the way we do things from consuming music to accessing information, designing products and engaging with the world around us. Would the success of Apple have been achieved with accountants in control?

On the supposition that accountants are not fit to run industry, why, the reader may ask, are accountants so dominant in UK business? One possible answer is that accountants are essential in exploiting every available tax loophole in minimising tax payments. General Electric (not to be confused with GEC), one of the largest corporations in America filed a 57,000 page federal tax return in 2011 and didn't pay taxes on $14 billion profit[5]. Apple's legal tax avoidance strategies were reported to have sheltered $94 billion from the US tax authorities according to a *Sunday Times* analysis[6]. Tax considerations apart, other legal techniques used in manipulating figures in annual accounts can be read in the book titled *Creative Accounting* by Ian Griffiths, published in 1986 under chapter headings that included: 'How to pilfer the pension fund', 'How to tamper with Taxation', 'How to fiddle foreign currency translation', ' How to operate off balance sheet financing' and 'How to sharpen share capital'. The latter technique involves companies buying back their own shares, a technique regularly used by GEC during the Weinstock era and nowadays very popular, having coincided with the rise of management incentive schemes based on increasing share value, or earnings per share. Why should this concern you? Money spent by buying back one's own shares is money that could have been spent in paying dividends to shareholders, a basic reason why many shareholders, especially pensioners, buy and hold shares in the first place.

Whatever arguments may be made as to whether all these accounting techniques are good or bad, it cannot be denied that they are basically a means of keeping the proceeds of wealth creation to a select few.

Should accountants be trusted to run business?

References:

[1] *Slide Rule*. Nevil Shute. Autobiography. ISBN 978-0-099-530176

[2] Wikipedia, Wolseley Aries.

[3] *Guardian* Newspaper Obituary 24.7.02

[4] *Apple Confidential 2.0:* Owen W. Linzmayer. No Starch Press.

[5] *Money Week*. Issue 566. Bill Bonner. Last word.

[6] *Daily Telegraph*. 27.1.13.

ENGINEERS
(Damned by the English language?)

In the UK, 'engineering' is defined as an industrial sector consisting of employers and employees, loosely termed as engineers, who range from semi-skilled and skilled trades workers to technicians and chartered engineers. In practice, in the UK, the term 'engineer' means anyone associated with any form of machinery and engineering is considered more as a trade than a profession. The BBC uses the word engineer to describe anyone involved in manual labour, such as digging up roads, for example.

As a result of this loose definition, it is believed that there are over two million people in Britain who have the title of engineer in their job description despite having limited qualifications[1].

The correct or more accurate definition of an engineer is 'a professional practitioner of engineering, concerned with applying scientific knowledge, mathematics and ingenuity to develop solutions for technical and practical problems'. Engineers are grounded in applied sciences, and their work in research and development is distinct from the basic research focus of scientists. The distinction between scientists and engineers is often lost to the detriment of the latter. UK engineers such as Barnes Wallis and R J Mitchell are invariably described as scientists. The term engineer and its subsequent status has been, and continues to be, a source of discontent with members of the many British Engineering Institutions. This is not the case in other European countries. In Continental Europe, the law limits the title to those who possess an engineering degree. The use of the title by others is illegal. In Italy, the title is limited to people who hold both an engineering degree and have passed a professional qualification examination.

It could be argued that the lack of status associated with engineering, both academically and socially, is a major reason why the UK lost, and will continue to lose its ranking in the industrial world.

At the start of the twentieth century, the lack of applied scientific know how, resulted in the UK having to rely on USA and Germany for the development of power generation using alternating current. The lack of scientific and associated know-how also resulted in the UK lagging far behind Germany in the chemical industry. The implications of the latter became apparent during the First World War when contrary to UK expectations Germany did not run out of nitrates required for the manufacture of explosives. The UK also had to be rescued by American technology during the Second World War. A much more thorough and detailed development of the above theme can be read in the books of the historian Correlli Barnett that include; *The Swordbearers, The Collapse of British Power, The Lost Victory* and *The Verdict of Peace.*

One possible explanation for the relatively poor state that the engineering profession finds itself in within the UK is that of the English language itself. English is the language of Shakespeare and beautiful poetry. English is a language rich in meanings and capable of rousing the nation when used by masters of it such as Lloyd George and Winston Churchill. Other languages no doubt will claim the same, but as we English don't speak them, we don't really know. Japanese is an interesting example. I never managed to get a bi-lingual Japanese person to explain which language was better at expressing poetry. What I did notice was that all the Japanese that I came into contact with at work were far superior in doing hand sketches and drawings when compared to their English peers. In spite of these and other considerations, the English language, as has been indicated by the term engineer, does seem to have a remarkable propensity for misunderstandings. What for example, do foreigners make of the words 'public school', 'industrial action' and 'compensation'? At face value, 'public schools' are schools for the public and by implication available to everyone. In reality they are private schools available only to a privileged few. On the face of it, 'industrial action' means getting things done in industry. In the UK it means exactly the opposite. The word 'compensation' is apparently straightforward. It means reimbursement for some form of setback suffered. I had my left femur broken in my teens, as a result of which I received compensation. The last thing one would expect is the word compensation being used to describe the exorbitant salary, pension arrangements, bonuses, and other benefits involved in finalising the payment package of some top executive.

The interpretation and double meanings of many English words has provided a very good living for many people in the entertainment industry and will no doubt continue to do so for the foreseeable future. The same applies to the legal industry. In fact it could be argued that it is the interests of the legal industry to have such a language in which to flourish. There do seem to be more lawyers in the Anglo-Saxon world than elsewhere. (Certainly more than in Japan for example.) Politicians use the language to full effect in order to appear all things to all people.

The disadvantage of having a language that has so many meanings for so many words, is that in committee meetings there often appears to be two or more issues being discussed under a given topic, without the participants realising it. One such topic is the word 'engineer'.

There is clearly a case to be made that UK engineers have been, and are damned by their own language. As a consequence their profession has suffered as has the UK economy itself.

References:

[1.]You say engineer, I say gas fitter – plumbers protest at BAE remarks. Amy Wilson. *Daily Telegraph* March 2, 2010.

EXTERNAL COMMUNICATION
(Lost in the post?)

In 1958, during the busy Christmas period, I, along with thousands of other school sixth formers in the UK, worked for the Post Office to help deliver the large quantities of seasonal mail. For many, this was their first experience of a real workplace and work practices. It was an annual event that benefited the students, the Post Office and the public.

In the early 1970s the company for whom I worked, entered joint ownership negotiations with an Italian company. During my visits to the head office of the Italian company in Milan, I noticed that the company routinely sent its mail over the border and had it posted from Switzerland. The company regarded the unionised Italian state run postal service unreliable. After the negotiations were concluded I subsequently experienced considerable problems with the Italian post when requesting, or transferring, details to and from the Italian company's factory situated in southern Italy. At that time in Italy, there were many frequent strikes both in state owned and private industries. I was in Milan when I became aware of a huge scandal involving the Italian postal service. Postal workers were accused of routinely and systematically opening and removing money from letters sent from abroad, in addition to selling large quantities of letters as waste paper. I recall thinking at the time how fortunate we were in the UK not to have such problems with our postal system.

In the 'Money Section' of *The Times* newspaper dated January 15, 2011, there was an article concerning tens of thousands of disgruntled customers who were being urged to claim compensation payments from the Royal Mail following the loss of more than two million parcels and letters lost or delayed. The article stated that the Royal Mail loses about 600,000 items of mail per week. What has happened to those missing or delayed letters?

One answer may be that some letters, considered potentially profitable by someone, are forwarded to places where they can be examined at leisure and their contents, such as account details, plastic cards and cheque books could either be noted or taken. Letters subsequently re-posted would never have been missed for a few days whilst those delivering dividends would of course never be delivered. Details of such a scenario were published on the 12 January 2011 in an article titled 'The scammers who open your post', in www.lovemoney.com.

For various reasons school sixth formers are no longer used to help deliver post during the busy Christmas period, as was the case during my schooldays. What would appear to be a simple straightforward business of collecting letters from one area to another for the benefit of customers, seems to have been perverted to provide benefits to others, whose interests are not quite the same, namely, legislators, unions and management.

The UK postal system that I knew in 1958 has changed. Has the Italian postal system that I knew in the early 1970s changed too?

E6

SQUEEZING ASSETS UNTIL THE PIPS SQUEAK
(Wealth creation UK style?)

'Where there's muck there's money', was a common expression I often heard in Lancashire, the area that I grew up in as a youngster.

Retired, living in Kent I regularly walked the dog through the grounds of an old large house where I often bumped into the long retired owner walking his dog too.

The house had outbuildings, a large garden and various fields amounting to approximately 15 acres on which sheep grazed. One day I noticed the house was up for sale for approximately £1 million. Upon meeting the owner, I expressed regret that he had to move, and we casually discussed the property market. The 15 acres were worth approximately £30 thousand and generated a nominal income of £300 pa from farmers, who used the land for sheep grazing. If the land had planning permission for housing, it would have been worth £15 million. In short, the possession of a piece of paper, allowing planning permission to build property on, would have resulted in an immediate increase in value of the land from £30 thousand to £15 million. Obtaining planning permits clearly result in opportunities to make huge amounts of money. This, in itself, is not the same as creating wealth, although for the individuals concerned it is.

During my early working years, the UK Government and Local Authorities created development areas to encourage the transfer of industry to those areas that were considered most needy. The Development Areas offered the opportunity to reorganise, pay off staff and relocate. Assets, more often than not outdated machinery, were moved from one area to another. Not only did this offer an opportunity for consolidation, the original land, usually owned, could be sold to property developers and the new premises and site could be leased at favourable rates. When benefits such as free rates periods had expired, it was not unknown for further moves to occur. Summarising, money could be made by basically moving muck around the country.

Some non-industrial companies, not slow to see opportunities, looked for old established companies where site values were undervalued, and repeated the same moves. The term 'asset stripping' became one of the expressions used to denote such activities. The repetition of such moves on a grander scale resulted in the creation of conglomerates, giant companies comprising a multitude of different types of companies who only had budget targets and accountancy reports in common. The success of one such conglomerate, now deceased, even received the editorial plaudits of the British Institution of Management (BIM) magazine *Management Today*.

German companies in the main continue to be run by engineers and tend to spend money on updating their premises and facilities. Many German companies remain under family control. The founders of such companies were invariably engineers, who had their offspring educated as engineers, a situation totally different from long since deceased similar British companies where the founder's offspring received the benefits of a classical education.

The proverbial man from Mars, comparing the UK and Germany, might ponder how, within a period of two generations, the UK, once the richest country in the world, on the winning side in two World Wars, could end up heavily in debt, and be of secondary importance in real economic terms to its former adversary. One answer could well be the different approach to wealth creation, one of which would appear to be illusory.

Translating the UK northern expression 'where there's muck there's money' into action by moving muck around the country, taking advantages of development grants, has clearly not created wealth in any real sense of the word. To justify such actions by using another common expression 'squeezing assets until the pips squeak', just adds insult to injury. Such actions do however encapsulate what was an all too common approach to wealth creation UK style, during my working life.

WHERE HAS ALL THE MONEY GONE?
(Creative Destruction?)

The Equitable Life Assurance Society (Equitable Life), the world's oldest mutual insurer, founded in 1762, pioneered the system upon which all life assurance schemes became based. The company became an obvious and preferred choice for both self-employed and company pension schemes.

The 1995 edition of *THE TIMES 1000 1995* describing itself on the front cover as, 'The indispensable Annual Review of the World's Leading Industrial and Financial Companies', has on its back cover a single advert for The Equitable Life.

Over half the back cover is dominated by a statement exclaiming:

HOW LONG WILL IT BE BEFORE EVERYONE'S LIVING THE EQUITABLE LIFE?

Beneath the statement are the following notes:

It's quite something to make it into the top 500 of The Times 1000.

The companies at the top not only know how to make money. They also know how to make it work for them.

Perhaps that's why more than half of the top 500 have chosen The Equitable for their employees' AVCs.

They know that the Equitable's contract conditions are flexible and free from any hidden traps.

They know about their excellent investment performance record.

And, perhaps most importantly, they know that The Equitable's low costs help to produce good investments returns.

It's no secret.

In all, more than 3,000 companies have a pension arrangement with The Equitable Life.

Will it be long before you're living The Equitable Life?

Past performance, however, is not a guarantee of future performance.

At the bottom of the advert was the name 'The Equitable Life' beneath which was the slogan, 'You profit from our principles'.

Five years later, in July 2000, the House of Lords upheld an Appeal Court ruling in the *'Equitable Life Assurance Society v Hyman'* case which resulted in Equitable Life closing for new business and putting itself up for sale as its assets were approximately £4.5 billion less than its commitments.

The *'THE TIMES 1000 1995'* inside contents make interesting reading too.

Two companies that I worked for during my career are shown to have a combined equity valuation of £15 billion. The two companies subsequently merged, and, fifteen years later in 2010, the resultant renamed company had an equity valuation of £2 billion, and a pension liability of £4 billion.

Where has all the money gone?

COME THE REVOLUTION
(What should you ask for facing a firing squad?)

There is always the possibility of a revolution. History shows that revolutions often start because a majority perceive that they are funding the extravagant lifestyle of a minority. Revolutions can also start following the repercussions when a Government is unable to honour its debts. I recall reading somewhere that one of the leaders of the Green Party opined that the UK could only support a population of 43 million. How this would be attained was not made clear. The Boy Scout's motto is: 'Be prepared'.

Towards the end of World War II, the Soviet Army came up against the German Sturmgewehr 44 (StG 44) assault rifle. This was the first successful weapon of its type and had a marked impact on the Eastern Front as it offered a greatly increased rate of fire compared with standard infantry rifles and could effectively engage targets at longer ranges than the MP40 (Schmeisser). The impact was such that the Russians desired an equivalent. The result was the Automat Kalashnikov assault rifle (AK-47).

In 1949, the AK-47 rifle was issued to the Soviet army. The rifle was rugged, compact, reliable and cheap to manufacture. Since that time, it is believed that over 70 million AK-47 rifles have been made. The life expectancy of the rifle is between 20 and 40 years dependant upon the conditions the rifle has been subjected to. Kalashnikov, the designer is reported to have said:

'Before attempting to create something new, it is vital to have a good appreciation of everything that exists in its field. I have had many experiences confirming this is so[1].'

In essence, Kalashnikov re-engineered the German StG 44.

In the 1960s the UK decided to replace the Belgian FN rifle with the SA-80, a rifle that would be designed and produced in the UK.

In the early 1970s the MoD (Ministry of Defence) lay down the specifications of the new gun that had to be fulfilled. The gun had to be light, cheap and accurate, with emphasis being placed on the latter. One would have thought that one of the fundamental considerations in drawing up a specification would be to consider the type of person who would be the ultimate user, namely a typical infantryman. Over ten percent of the population are left-handed. The composition of infantrymen would be no different. There are advantages in this natural mix, as it is believed that a squad of soldiers has a better chance of survival in an ambush if it has a few left-handed soldiers in it. This is because left-handed soldiers automatically carry their weapons pointed in the opposite direction from their right-handed counterparts.

The SA-80 was designed from the start to be fired from the right shoulder with spent cartridges ejected sideways. In other words it was designed for right-handed soldiers only. The rifle was officially pronounced fit for service in January 1984 and was formally accepted by the in army in 1985. During that year two SA-80 rifles were sent to the German gun makers Heckler & Koch for training purposes. Shortly afterwards the officer who had sent the rifles received a phone call from the Germans informing him that the guns fired bullets when the rifles were dropped. The officer was also asked whether or not he was aware of this. The officer admitted that he wasn't, and subsequently obtained a gun from the armoury and dropped it. The gun went off. In short, a major safety flaw in a British rifle that had supposedly undergone exhaustive testing and had been accepted into army service, was found by the Germans, upon receiving two of them.

The production of the rifle was another issue. The SA-80 production line was reported to be utterly and totally unreliable and could not meet the required quality standards. Privatisation did not help matters, 1,200 of the workforce in Enfield were fired as the new owners BAE transferred the production facilities to Nottingham.

A reality check came with the first Gulf War in 1991. Guns jammed, parts fell off, plastic parts melted, cartridge cases wouldn't eject properly and locking pins easily pulled out for gun cleaning, could, if forced back, puncture the gun casing, rendering the gun useless. There were anecdotal tales of soldiers swapping their SA80s for Kalashnikovs.

In 2000 the gun was contracted to Heckler & Koch, a subsidiary of BAE at the time, to sort the problems out. The contract cost was believed to be £80m. The SA-80 rifle had 83 modifications in 18 years and cost the taxpayer almost £500m[2].

Summarising, the Russians, after re-engineering what they considered the best rifle available, designed, developed and put into service the AK-47, all within a period of four years.

The current British SA-80 army rifle was accepted by the British Army 26 years after the acceptance of the Kalashnikov AK-47 by the Soviet Army. This is the same time period that it took to progress from bi-planes in WWI to the V2 rocket in WWII.

At the time of writing the war in Afghanistan is still in progress. Observant TV viewers will have noticed our troops carry their rifles to fire from the right shoulder, and they will have also noticed how they are exposed when firing through a gap in a wall that is approached from the right.

In 2010 the MoD came under criticism to the extent that it was suggested as being unfit for purpose. The criticism was put into perspective when bonuses of £37 million awarded to the MoD Civil Service, were defended vigorously by the Government of the day.

If the reader ever finds him, or herself, in the unfortunate position of facing a firing squad and is allowed a final request, the reader should ask to be shot by left-handed marksmen using the 1985 model of the British Army SA-80 rifle. The rifles could be dropped whilst being issued, in which case they would go off and hopefully kill someone other than the reader. In the event that this does not occur and you finally face the firing squad, do you believe that the marksmen will be able to shoot straight knowing that they themselves, being left-handed, will be hit on the head by the ejected cartridges, unless of course the guns jam. In either eventuality you the reader will in all probability live.

Should the officer in charge of the execution squad be especially accommodating regarding your final request, you could add that you would like the execution squad to be first put on a five mile romp through bogs wearing British Army boots as specified and supplied in the Korean War. I recall as a young boy following events in the Korean War, reading in the *News Chronicle*, that our troops were buying boots from the Americans because their own boots were useless. The boots either leaked or their soles kept falling off, or so I understood at the time.

References:

[1].Soviet Small Arms and ammunition. David Naumovich Bolotin, pp 123-124, Translation. Publisher: Finnish Arms Museum Foundation.

[2] Article titled, Off Target by James Meek. *The Guardian* newspaper.10.10.02.

POSTSCRIPT

This book has a triple purpose. The first is to give a feel for what it was like to have worked in a UK manufacturing environment from the mid twentieth to the twenty-first century, a period of unrelenting manufacturing decline. The second has been to illustrate that the service industries created, filling the gap so to speak, have not been an effective substitute. Last, but not least, to show that the continuous decline of manufacturing as a force within the UK economy can be attributed to persistent poor political decisions and beliefs that are endemic within the UK educational and political system.

To have continued earning a living in manufacturing during my lifetime in the UK when industries were collapsing around you could be likened to that of following the 'Old American West' advice on the art of survival, namely, keeping one town ahead of the chasing posse. This approach may have been satisfactory for an individual, but overall it is clear that for most people this would have been impracticable, if not impossible. Massive job losses have been incurred as a result, as has the ability to create wealth by manufacturing goods.

Sir John Rose, the ex-Chief Executive of Rolls Royce is reported to have said:

"There are only three ways to create wealth, you can dig it up, you can grow it, or you can convert something in order to add value, everything else is just moving it about."

During my working life the UK appears to have ceased digging it up, couldn't be bothered to pick what little we did grow and finally, legislated, hounded, sold and closed down the ability to convert things. The UK as a nation appear to be content building, buying and selling houses to each other, in effect moving ourselves around and being paid in monopoly money.

In my lifetime it has been a political belief that manufacturing decline is inevitable and that losses in manufacturing can be offset by the growth in wealth creation by the provision of services, especially financial services.

Much of the growth of service industries have been created as a result of incessant laws passed by Parliament. It could be argued that many of these service industries far from serving the consumer seem to have been created for the benefit of those running the services themselves, self-service in fact.

The essence of the UK's value and belief system is perhaps best encapsulated in the contrasting treatment accorded to Thomas "Tommy" Harold Flowers and Sir James "Jimmy" Wilson Vincent Savile, during their respective lifetimes.

Tommy Flowers was an engineer who during World War II conceived, designed and built 'Colossus', the world's first programmable electronic computer. Colossus helped solve encrypted high-level German messages and shortened the duration of the War. Following the end of World War II, Flowers was awarded the MBE and granted £1,000, an amount that did not cover his own personal investment. As a result of the Official Secrets Act, Flowers was unable to pursue a career based on his wartime work, and the Colossus machines were eventually destroyed without the machines being made available to a nascent industry. Flowers' work was not acknowledged until he had passed retirement age.

Jimmy Savile was a disc jockey and TV personality who raised an estimated £40 million for charities, enriching himself in the process. In 1971 Savile was awarded the OBE, a higher award than the MBE, and knighted in 1990. Jimmy Savile was eulogised by the BBC, his employer, on prime time TV during the Christmas period 2011-12, following his death.

In short, the UK is no country for Engineers.